*Tony Luongo*

Joseph Torra is the author of *Gas Station,* a novel, and *Keep Watching the Sky,* a collection of poetry. He lives in Somerville, Massachusetts.

By the same author

*Keep Watching the Sky* (poetry)
*Gas Station* (fiction)

# JOSEPH TORRA

**VICTOR GOLLANCZ**

**LONDON**

A Gollancz Paperback Original

First published in Great Britain in 2000 by Victor Gollancz
An imprint of Orion Books Ltd
Orion House, 5 Upper Saint Martin's Lane,
London WC2H 9EA

A CIP catalogue record for this book is
available from the British Library

ISBN 0 575 06848 5

Printed and bound by
The Guernsey Press Co. Ltd, Guernsey, C. I.

For William Corbett

Three weeks is the longest I ever went without taking a shit it was in boot camp the first time I went away from home graduating high school in June September I joined in the Voke I took carpentry and could've found work as an apprentice but in the Marines I could go someplace far away like Korea and I knew I'd never see Korea from Somerville I loved basic training but being away from home the change of food hard exercise and officers up and down your ass every second I couldn't shit I didn't worry at first cause I'd gone a week without shitting before but when it started getting near two weeks the cramping got real bad and I couldn't eat I went to see the doctor who said it was almost impossible to go three weeks but since I was a little kid it was nothing to go two or three days and I could remember times when it was a week or more though it never went this long he gave me some stuff syrup to drink and said it would clean me right out I took it for three days nothing happened the cramping got so bad I could barely stand and thought I would wash out of basic training then finally at the end of the third week after nights doubled over from the cramps and long days I never thought I would live to the see end of we were out in the field on drills it was pouring rain they had us crawling around in mud that's the only reason nobody knew I shit myself the way I did I couldn't control it it poured like a fountain I just laid there on the ground it flowed and flowed suddenly the sergeant was over me screaming to get moving so I got up and ran down a gully and pretended to fall into a stream so I could get my pants washed up if anyone knew what happened I would have been tossed out it was the strangest feeling on the muddy ground thinking every last bit of my insides was oozing out of me not being able to move until it ran its course when I graduated boot camp Ma and my sisters and brother Peter came down to see the ceremony Ma carried a dish of macaroni and meatballs on the plane she said if I could only eat her food I'd go to the bathroom better I wasn't away that long but it was the first time Ma looked old hunched over tired squinting to see behind her glasses the recruits went crazy for Gina I wouldn't let any of those animals near her and made her button her blouse Peter always quiet didn't want nothing to do with the barracks and mess tours like most boys his age and Josie hiding behind her glasses tending to Ma talked about Frank in prison when they visited him they brought food the prisoners loved Ma's cooking in boot camp I got into the discipline yes sir no sir push-ups running and those motherfucking drill sergeants up your ass I'd be proud if a son of mine wanted to serve I learned respect from Ma telling us to always be respectful to elders and I called elders by Mr or Mrs or Sir or Mam and at work the guys called me an ass-kiss cause I called the division managers by Mr Santisi or Mr Fournier instead of their first names like everyone else but it wasn't ass kissing they were my boss and older than me other recruits didn't like the regiment of training or the drill sergeants and when the sergeant came yelling and banging in the middle of the night we had to stand next to our bunks at attention waiting to be inspected God help the guy

who left something out of place they never could
nail me for anything my mother thought if she
could only talk to the general or something they
might let me get stationed close to Boston if they
knew she needed me nearby being the oldest son
which I wasn't but Frank was in jail first I went
to California then we got shipped to Korea a few
of the companies went to Vietnam but no one
had even heard of it yet from then on I had it
made I was with a construction company we did
maintenance work around the base every month
we went out to the field for drills I was there for
sixteen months Ma was different when I got
back from Korea she lost the sight in her right
eye said if that's what God wants then that's
what she wants I saw relatives and they wanted
to hear about Korea and the Marines but it wore
off then I found a job at Pratt's retail store
Central Square Cambridge in the display department I missed Korea it was the first time in my
life I was on my own I mostly kept to myself in
free time went out to strip bars to see these
shows with girls putting snakes and bottles and
whatever else up inside them I drank a lot and
when I was horny I got a blow job for pennies
those girls let you come all over their faces then I

would get rice somewhere fried rice I love fucking fried rice I got the biggest order and staggered back to the base eating the rice leaving a
trail of it behind for pennies they let you come
all over their face and the personnel manager at
Pratt's said they needed someone who could do
nitty-gritty construction work for the display
people so I spent my days measuring spaces and
building little wooden constructions and then
Joe Letto and Celeste King decorated over them
with women's purses or men's shirts or the latest
model vacuum cleaner I wanted to move out of
Ma's apartment Frank moved back in there the
girls were sharing a room and Frank Peter and
me had to share a room this guy named Danny
Kelly who worked in the shoe department was
looking for a roommate so I moved into the second floor of a three story on Porter Street and
walked to work in less than five minutes I always
wanted to do Celeste but never had the chance
when I first started at Pratt's she was dating Bill
Nardella the division manager of the paint
department who was just going through a
divorce there was something about her got me
wild she knew it too the tease wearing those
mini-skirts and wasn't ashamed to climb a lad-

der or bend over digging for something in the display room I told her on no uncertain terms she smiled not on your best day Danny Kelly was probably the best friend I ever had we lived together for two years Danny was kind of wild he liked to drink and smoke pot he got it on with guys and chicks I never had much money cause I was on a salary in the display department it wasn't very good but the benefits were and I tried to give my mother any extra cash I could to help keep her going Gina graduated and got a job at an insurance company downtown Peter quit school and got a job working at Schrafts Candy Company in Sullivan Square so they were helping with some money Frank was living with a woman in Everett then they had a fight one night and he beat her up and the cops in Everett were looking for him so he moved back in with Ma the hardest thing was to give money to Ma and make sure Frank didn't get his hands on it everything went to gambling Frank had only the clothes on his back when he lived with a chick he didn't pay no rent he was supposed to be looking for a job cause he was on parole but mostly he hung around his usual haunts like Pal Joey's on the hill the job at Pratt's was working out for me

I liked display and got to work all over the store and there were some hot chicks working in those departments in a few months I started fucking this young one in the candy department she was a little screwy a few of the guys had already been at her including Bill Nardella while he was dating Celeste but Celeste never knew and this chick she did Danny and me not at once but we were both in bed with her and she took Danny first and then me I'm not sure she was even legal age she said she was eighteen man did she know what she was doing I wanted them all young ones old ones May Sullivan the division manager of women's was in her early fifties and she was so sexy I told her I'd marry her any time she'd have me but she said she would never marry again she did her playing outside the store one of those people who can keep themselves from shitting where they eat at that time everyone was smoking pot it made me dizzy and sick to my stomach it was no good for me in bed it made me go limp and all scared but people said it was great for sex but the thing about sex for me I never have a problem just getting to it I believe it's what everybody's always thinking about anyway I don't care who they are or where they are if

you're working you think of sex if you're driving
down the street and you see a chick you feel that
fire and it's only then it can be quenched it's pure
in a way and I never needed drugs for it I'd rather
fuck sober than drunk and then all the guys
started growing their hair long I didn't but in a
year it was like the Corps was a strange part of
the past that I wasn't sure happened though Ma
kept my letters and there was still my color por-
trait in dress blues sitting on her mantle I only
remembered images a girl putting a snake up her
cunt being down on my belly in the mud shitting
my insides out one night Danny brought this
chick home and we both did her while we were
getting it on he made a move for me it was the
first time and I didn't know what to do but to my
surprise the chick dug it so I got into it too then
the next day I felt fucked up like there was something wrong I couldn't talk to Danny for a few
days finally I told him how I felt he said there
was nothing wrong with any of it I told him
about Frank and me how Frank used to make me
do him when I was a kid but I didn't think Frank
did any guys no more it was just kind of being
young and exploring different things I tried to
keep myself in shape being in the Marines I got

built up for the first time in my life my arms got
so big from all those push-ups I must have done
a million all you had to do was look at that
sergeant the wrong way and you were doing fifty
so I did push-ups I ran after coming back I
stopped drinking as much as I did in Korea
Frank liked to tear one on once in a while then
all hell broke loose Pa was the great drinker
when we were kids Ma would march us into
whatever bar he was in Frank Gina me Peter Ma
pregnant with Josie I wore Frank's hand-me-
down clothes the shoes were so worn out my
toes stuck through she said she wanted to
embarrass him in front of his friends so he
would be ashamed and come home but it never
worked when he finally came home he roughed
her up I don't remember a time when there was
money we lived on macaroni and bread except
on Sundays Pa hit Peter who needed glasses but
Pa wouldn't pay for them and something was
wrong with his hearing too we all knew at
school the nurse sent notices home that he failed
the hearing test Pa said he was stupid and when
he was drunk he told Peter things like I should
have flushed you down the toilet when you were
born I get so sick now if I drink too much but

once I have a couple I don't stop I'll go all night but with me I never needed it like Pa did and the stuff makes me happy not mean cause Peter was the kindest kid who wouldn't hurt a bug besides Ma he got the worse from Pa Pa if he loved anything besides the bottle he loved Sunday dinners and Ma every Sunday made her gravy with all the sausages and meatballs and pork I remember once or twice when we all sat around the table at our old Marshall Street apartment and ate Sunday dinner together Ma and Pa Frank me Gina and Peter this was before Josie was born and Pa didn't drink too much and Ma was happy and Frank was still a boy in junior high but before she left Pa he was usually never around or when he was it was late in the day or after we went to bed he came home drunk wanting Ma to boil him some fresh macaroni and make sure the gravy was hot they gave us so much food in the Marines no matter where we were even in the field the cooks laid it on heavy steak and eggs for breakfast pancakes huge lunches and dinners of steaks and roasts and chickens I was always hungry all I could ever think about in Korea was getting my off time and getting blow jobs and fried rice it was so hard to jerk off one thing about the

military for all the good is you get no privacy Ma
put up with a lot from Pa drinking and sometimes whoring even the occasional beatings but
two weeks after Gina turned twelve I remember
cause Gina was starting to grow tits she kept us
home from school one day and after Frank and
Pa left she pulled out a suitcase she had been
hiding in the basement which was already full of
clothes and marched us to South Station we took
a train to New York City this woman who spoke
no English and her four children aged fifteen
thirteen twelve and ten Frank had just quit
school and had a job at A & P Supermarket and
she left him behind with Pa Ma found us a room
above a bakery in an Italian neighborhood and
she applied for welfare but it didn't come for a
while the owners of the bakery this husband and
wife felt bad for us and gave us day-old bread we
ate nothing but day-old bread and milk though
there were times back at home when that's all we
ate the doctor said that's why Josie had rickets
and took cod-liver oil finally Ma got on welfare
and somehow the welfare people got in touch
with Ma's sister Lena in Boston and a while after
we were on welfare my aunt and Frank took
a train and found us in New York City they

wanted to bring us back but Ma was afraid Pa would kill her like he threatened he would if she left him Frank and my aunt brought articles from the newspapers with a photo of Pa and the headlines about where did Anna Luongo and her children disappear to a picture of Pa acting all sad saying his heart was broke and he would die without his family Ma couldn't believe it when I told her in Italian what it said in the articles she didn't want to go home but my aunt had legal papers told Ma all she had to do was sign them and Pa could never go near her again for two days Ma kept saying she would never go back but then finally she signed the papers and we went home to Boston and Ma went on welfare and never saw Pa again only once did he see us after that it was a Sunday afternoon he took us to the North End we ate spaghetti and walked around the feast but then Pa started drinking and kept drinking and didn't get us home til after midnight so Ma wouldn't let him take us out ever again he died a year later Ma wouldn't even go to his funeral none of us did except Frank I'll never get over how we had to be on welfare I swore when I was a kid that when I grew up I would take care of everybody so

nobody would need nothing it wasn't that we
needed all that much it was the idea we were on
welfare Ma said sometimes she wished she
stayed in Italy cause there was no welfare there
everyone took care of everybody I loved it when
we lived in New York City and roamed Times
Square looking in porno shops and movie houses
until the cops or a bouncer chased me off everywhere was guys chicks and sex I mean that's
what they're there for one thing no bullshit like
let's go for a drink or to the movies or out to dinner where everybody's on the make anyway you
go to a restaurant you see this hot chick sitting at
a table you get a sexy waitress and what do you
think you think I'd do her in a second the chicks
think the same thing when a good looking waiter
walks up to a table some chick sitting there for
dinner's thinking how she'd do him it's crazy
what it does to you in New York City I couldn't
get privacy in the little apartment me and Peter
slept on a mattress on the floor in the front room
Ma and the girls slept in a bed in the one bedroom I got myself worked up in Times Square
had to wait til the middle of the night when I
was sure that Peter was sleeping I sat in the old
torn chair Ma sat in during the day and did it

there so when Frank and my aunt came to bring us home I missed New York City in Boston Frank took me downtown where it was kind of like Times Square people were on the make and there were porno stores theaters and strip joints he got me into a movie that's the first time I saw a porno movie this black and white thing all guys in the theater jerking off Frank too that's what everyone comes here for he said so once I realized no one was paying attention to me anyway I jerked off too being on welfare once a month we had to go to the welfare office we got a box of food mostly stuff we didn't eat the coffee was weak we didn't like peanut butter but there was things like lard and milk we laughed going through the box at the macaroni and cheese and canned beef stew Ma put it away in case there was another depression it was after Pa died Frank started getting into more serious trouble he broke into a furniture store and got caught the owner didn't press charges so the police let him go but when he robbed the Sunoco gas station at the foot of Broadway they sent him to reform school in Billerica everybody said Frank was pretty stupid to rob a gas station in his own neighborhood I was the first one in the

family to finish high school we had a party Ma
cooked a great dinner and invited relatives most
of them told me that now I was the one who had
to take care of the family it was up to me I could
have made more as a carpenter's apprentice and
lived home but there wasn't any room if I joined
the service I could send money home when
Frank was arrested for robbery a second time
they sent him to Concord prison for three years
he was never the same after that time he spent in
Concord what I liked most about the Corps was
the discipline that's what helped me so much in
my life on my job at Pratt's Mr Sanford the personnel manager said I was a model employee I
was never out sick or late in all my years there
display was easy compared with the Marines
didn't have to be in until eight got a twenty-
minute coffee break in the morning a forty-five-
minute lunch then another twenty-minute coffee
break in the afternoon and with all the standing
around bullshitting with everyone especially the
ladies on the first-floor lingerie and all the nude
mannequins so many jokes you can make so
when you got down to it I was only actually
working about five or six hours a day with
nobody up my ass and all these beautiful chicks

from sixteen to sixty I got out at five with
Saturdays and Sundays off Sundays I went to
Ma's and brought her money she cooked a gravy
and we all ate together except Frank he only
showed up at Ma's if he needed a bed he usually
had a girlfriend Ma's was his last choice I always
believed the most important thing you can do
with your family is eat together and that's part
of the problem with families these days everybody is so busy nobody has meals together any
more all you hear about is fast food take-out
now people eat in their cars I went over once or
twice during the week to check on Josie see how
she was doing in school or make sure Gina was-
n't wearing her skirts too short or smearing too
much make-up on her face sometimes I would
bring Chinese food but the only thing Ma liked
was spare ribs so I always got an extra order just
for her this will be my dinner she said and she
could eat every rib down to the bone mostly she
liked to cook and eat her own food pasta-fagioli
or roasted chicken usually Friday and Saturday
nights I went down the Zone alone watched a
movie and a strip show the girl in the candy
department went a little loony taking drugs
emptying the nitro-tanks for filling kiddy bal-

loons to get high she took a liking to me but I
stopped getting on with her she still came on to
me and asked about Danny and one day she told
me that she and Danny were still getting it on
and Danny told her a few things about him and
me and she wanted to get it on with the three of
us again that's the first time there was a real rift
between me and Danny cause he never told me
he was still doing her he had no right to tell her
about what happened with him and me and that
chick it's not that I didn't like what happened sex
is sex I don't care who you are if you're a guy
and you're blindfolded someone starts sucking
your dick it will get hard it doesn't matter if it's a
guy or a chick but Danny talking about me and
him to somebody else like that pissed me off I
told him and he said I always took this stuff too
serious and he'd been thinking about us making
it together again just the two of us together I
didn't like the idea but I tried it one night after
we went to the Zone when we got home it was
good but it didn't feel the same way as when the
chick was there I was thinking maybe I was
queer Danny said it was just sex don't think
about it so much then he started seeing this chick
who worked in the catalogue department but she

wouldn't let the two of us do her at once but she told Danny she would do one of us while the other watched so that's what we did but then she started showing up at our apartment in the middle of the night acting crazy she was missing work and got fired the last time I saw her was a couple of years later late one night on Mass. Ave. in the center meridian wandering aimless high on pills she didn't recognize me she came from a rich family in Hamilton once she was in a mental hospital for a while she had a horse and the riding clothes I wanted her to dress up and use that crop on me but she wouldn't go for it when Pa was in a good mood he played the mandolin and sang one night after he came home drunk and started playing Ma told him to stop cause he'd wake everybody up he smashed his mandolin to pieces on the kitchen floor sometimes he gave us all a penny he said he picked from a penny tree in the yard then once Gina and Peter went to the window where Pa was sweeping in the yard they asked him could they have a penny off of the tree and Pa walked over to the window threw the broom at them and cut Gina above the eye she still has a little scar she's a beautiful girl my sister but he gave her this scar

the Asian chicks were small their cunts tiny they
don't have much hair on their bodies but they
could take it all when I was doing Joyce in ladies'
make-up she blew me but she wouldn't let me do
anything I had to lean back on the bed then she
would blow me if I tried to rub her tits or hair
she would push my hand away she didn't want
me to touch her while she was doing me I met
her mother and she was a looker too both
blondes with tight bodies and Joyce told me that
she and her mother used to go out together and
pick up guys they wouldn't do them together
wolfing her mother called it that's a little fucked
up if you ask me then she started fucking Mr
Aria the controller and dropped me he was a
good looking guy Mr Aria quiet type but he was
fooling around with more chicks in the store
than anybody when I was a kid in winter we
sledded down Winter Hill on cardboard boxes
we couldn't afford no sleds and when we got
home Ma made hot chocolate told us stories
when she was a girl her mother sent her to the
baker's for bread and before she left her mother
spit on the ground and told her to hurry because
if the spit dried up before she got back it meant
that something terrible was going to happen to

her when Frank did what he did to Gina Gina hit
him over the head with a rolling pin so hard it
took twenty stitches he never went near her
again I told him if he did I'd kill him she was
coming out of the shower he pulled her towel off
saying how nice she was looking all grown up I
never talked with him about what happened
when we were young but I thought about it it
wasn't right but I was young Frank was my big
brother I idolized him then it was before he
started getting into trouble after I got back from
the Marines one night he was trying to get
money off Ma I was there and told him to leave
her alone and quit bleeding her and he told me
to keep out of it and called me a few names but I
think he knew that since I was in the Marines I
was able to handle myself because I called him
out and he backed down but it upset Ma to see
us fighting she said it was her fault and sometimes she thought maybe she should never had
us Frank hit his girlfriends he only dated women
who liked getting hit he said all he needed to do
was talk to a chick for a few minutes he could
tell whether she liked it rough he took as much
money from them as he could Gina said he was
doing a few odd jobs for a local gang I asked her

what kind of jobs she said she didn't know when
I asked Frank about it he said I was crazy the day
Bobby Kennedy was shot I got my five-year pin
at Pratt's during one of the monthly storewide
meetings held in the furniture department I
always loved the Kennedys and if John wasn't
killed like he was a lot of the stuff that happened
in the sixties I don't think would happen I loved
the storewide meetings the girls were wearing
mini-skirts and sat with their legs crossed on the
plush sofas and Mr Sullivan the store manager
made a little speech some jokes and announced
the next big promotion talked up the profit-shar-
ing plan which Pratt's was famous for then he
handed out pins and Hank Bell was retiring from
furniture he had thirty years in with over a hundred thousand in his profit sharing there was a
party at the Adam Bronk House restaurant
before I was married I always went to the parties
it was a good time to get to know the chicks better by the end of the night married or single
folks were dancing drunk cheek to cheek and
kissing in the dark corners someone was always
retiring or receiving a service pin they said the
best job to have at Pratt's was big-ticket salesman these were the guys who sold the major

appliances washers dryers stoves and refrigera-
tors they worked on straight commission the
best of them made more money than anyone in
the store except for the manager they were
always fighting over sales and customers they
would stand at the bottom of the escalator
yelling out at the people coming down washer or
dryer today each trying to get to the customer
first the manager was called in to break up arguments over who stole whose customer it was like
entertainment and if there was some kind of
fiasco it didn't take long for the word to get
around the store and if you could you went
down to catch the excitement the management
liked keeping the guys at each other's throats to
keep their teeth sharp pity the browser when one
of them put the hook into you there was no way
out sometimes people would buy something just
to be free of it then call and cancel when they got
home when I had my yearly personnel visit with
Mr Sanford and he told me again that I was the
model employee I mentioned that I might like to
switch over to sales at some time in the future he
seemed amused and said that he thought I was
perfect in display I mentioned that I might like to
sell big-ticket items many people would like to

sell big ticket but it wasn't for everyone he said and there were people waiting to get into big ticket from other departments besides those guys would eat me alive I told him I'd like to be considered anyway working with Celeste got me so horny once she said she'd have drinks with me and after a few we made out she said she dug me but knew I was only after one thing and both of us being in the same department it wouldn't work but she wore those short skirts and tight blouses then she cut off her long hair which I didn't like at first but then I got used to it and thought it was sexy everyone said Joe Letto was queer the way he dressed in colorful suits and shoes he got his nails manicured and colored his hair red brown and talked a little like a chick but he denied it all the years we worked together I never saw him with a girlfriend he was funny liked to joke around and talk about sex like me he listened to my stories always said something funny back he was about fifty when I met him told me about when he was growing up rich and how when he was a boy he had to dress in a suit for dinner they had a butler and a maid he never really knew his parents cause he was raised by a nanny Joe said he didn't really have to work even

though there was less money than there used to
be he just did it to keep busy when I told him
stories about growing up poor he said that he
wished he had my mother and that family meant
different things to different people I think family
is the most important thing in life it was my
mother keeping us together as safe as she could
what saved us except for Frank but there are guys
like Frank who come from rich families too so
who knows only thing I do know is as long I
remember I couldn't think of too much else
besides sex I mean at some point no matter what
I was doing or who I was with or where my mind
wandered before long it was back to sex I knew
that someone had to keep the family together
and if it wasn't for the Marines I'm not sure I
would have had the discipline to do it maybe
Frank would have been a different guy if he
joined the Marines when he quit school but
things just happened the way they did when I
first laid eyes on Audry she had on a pair of tight
jeans and a halter-top it was one of those swel-
tering days she just started working in the marking room upstairs in the warehouse and it didn't
have no air conditioner it's where every single
piece of merchandise that came into the store

was inventoried given a merchandise number
and price tag on my way to coffee break I got
sidetracked when I saw her tight ass and bare
back Lillian the veteran of the marking room
knew me like a book and said it didn't take me
long when I went in nosing around she introduced us and I asked Audry did she fool around
and she said it all depended I asked on what she
said I'm not sure it's any of your business Lillian
laughed and said she's got your number already
meantime I was dating Laura Murphy who was
probably the love of my life she worked part-
time in customer service and was going to college she was smart Laura was her father owned
Murphy's Funeral home on Broadway they had
money and I always felt one of the reasons me
and Laura didn't work out was she thought I was
beneath her she dumped me for a guy who just
started law school after a year that we were
going out the greatest sex I ever had was with
Laura we used to fuck in the morning in the
afternoon and night hot days in that Porter
Street apartment sweat pouring off us soaking
the sheets she always said no one ever did her
like I did her and that she loved me and would
always love me but it just couldn't work out

between us it crushed me I couldn't eat or sleep I
had to take tonic to shit once a week it went on
for weeks I couldn't jerk off I lost weight at work
everybody asked was I all right and the problem
with the store was everyone knew your business
it bothered me knowing they all knew Laura
dumped me I confided a lot in Joe Letto he was a
friend through it and in all the years we worked
together I never saw him go out with anyone
after work for drinks or go to any of the parties
but two different nights he took me out after
work and we went for some food and a drink
and he let me talk and said he was sorry to hear
it and it must be very painful Joe always said
that love is a misunderstanding between two
fools and even though he knew it he took the
bait every time that's why they made bars and
we went to the Napoleon Club which I heard of
but never been inside of there were mostly guys
about Joe's age or older and real young dudes
there was this big piano bar and everyone sat
around drinking Martinis and Manhattans
singing songs from shows and movies I was
uncomfortable at first but after three quick
bourbon and cokes I was singing I'm a yankee
doodle dandy arm in arm with a group of old

queers swaying back and forth with them all of
us heartbroken one way or another one loved
someone that didn't love him one loved someone
who loved him but was married Joe never mentioned anything about those nights again and I
didn't neither but he helped me through a rough
time and I'll never forget him he was the one
who told me to keep putting the bug in Mr
Lentine and Mr Sanford's ear about getting out
of display and working out on the sales floor he
said I had a great personality I would be good at
it so I told the display manager Mr Lentine he
was surprised but if he could help me he would
the next year when I had my annual meeting
with Mr Sanford I asked him again about going
out on the sales floor he said you are really serious about this aren't you and I told him I was
that's why I kept telling him every time I saw him
he said give it a little time he'd look into things
then somehow the guys in major appliances got
wind of my intentions and started needling me
saying things like so you want to play with the
big boys but I didn't pay them any mind Ma was
living with Peter and the girls Peter was working
the overnight shift at Schrafts it was for the best
he quit school he had a hard time there in a

special class but they liked him at the factory and they loved Gina at the insurance company she got a raise almost right away Josie said she wanted to be a nurse so she was in the state college Gina Peter and me paid for her books and tuition and in her spare time she took care of Ma who was proud that Josie was in college and said it was hard to believe girls in college but it was good Josie was smart cause God didn't give her much to look at and her chances of finding a husband were not too good in time I got over Laura but I never forgot her whenever I thought of her over the years I got this drooping sensation in my stomach that must be what love is when you can't stop thinking of someone and all you want to do is be with them fucking sweating and swallowing each other but maybe that's only sex not love where do you separate the two if being of one self can also be of the other and the other being of one self can also be of two this is the kind of stuff Danny would say when he was smoking pot I thought it was a bunch of crap there was love and there was sex sometimes you had sex with someone you loved Danny also liked to watch television when he was high he said it made everything more intense but that

shit just made me scared and hungry in the middle of fucking on it I lost my train of thought it's
hard to say how much Pa's beating on Peter had
to do with Peter being slow Ma said she blamed
Pa for Peter's problems but Peter was always
slow slow to learn how to talk and when he
talked he talked funny when Pa was drunk and
beat Peter up Ma tried to help but Pa hit her too
if I did anything I got smacked Frank was big
enough to take on Pa but he never did he said it
wasn't right to hit your father but it was all right
for a father to hit his kids Frank kept magazines
under his mattress he let me look at them when
he wanted me to do him it was all right what him
and me did he said between brothers we needed
to know what it was like I never swallowed he
tried to get me to I just spit it out into the rag he
kept beside his bed he called it his goo-rag
always keep a goo-rag near your bed he said the
girls liked Frank the worse he treated them the
more they liked him I never understood it but
this buddy of mine in the Marines used to say
the same thing once you tell them you love them
you lose no matter who the chick is the worse
you treat her the better she likes you but I loved
chicks and never wanted to treat them bad Frank

said that's why my heart was always getting broken I never saw Frank's heart get broken when the welfare lady came to our New York apartment we didn't have a real bath so we had lice in our hair she gave Ma a shampoo and we spent a day with Ma scrubbing our heads over the cold water kitchen sink with water she warmed on the two-burner stove Ma cried cause she felt so ashamed the lady must think she was a bad mother from then on I always had this thing about bugs in my hair and being clean so I took at least two showers a day and spent a lot of time in front of the mirror pushing my hair aside with my hands looking for the little things never found one since that time in New York and Ma said this life you give me God you must be testing me and in New York she first said to me I was her boy who would make her proud so she wouldn't have to live her life in disgrace and I always remembered that for a while Audry and me played cat and mouse she knew I was after her but she kept her distance finally one day I got her to have coffee with me we made small talk my usual questions like do you fool around and all that didn't amuse her and when our time was up I said so we going to get together or what and she said thanks but it wasn't a good time she just got over a relationship and not interested in dating anyone from the store I kept after her while screwing around with a couple of different chicks Joe Letto said it was possible that I could wear it out so I should slow down Audry was kind of plain with long brown hair and no make-up but she had a great body and knew how to wear clothes to show it at work she hung out with people from the marking room and never went out after work or to work parties Danny decided he was going to California and gave his notice at Pratt's he was going to see the west so Peter moved in with me and it gave the girls and Ma more room at the apartment I talked with Peter about sex but he didn't seem interested don't you like girls I said oh yeah he liked girls but he got embarrassed one night I took him to the Zone I thought he was still a virgin he said he wasn't and did it twice with a girl from Schrafts he didn't like the Zone and wanted to go I got him into a bar even though he was under age but he ran out when one of the strippers spread her pussy in front of him when he had a few drinks he could get angry and start saying things about Pa how it wasn't right the way he treated everybody I knew it wasn't right but that was in the past you couldn't do anything about changing it his face turned red his eyes flared behind his thick glasses poor Peter I always hoped he would find a woman who would take care of him but I knew he might always need one of us I missed Danny cause with Peter it was more like home again we went to see Ma and the girls on Sunday for macaroni and at least another night during the week Peter went over on other nights too I started my day off with sit-ups and push-ups and still counted out like we did in the Marines staying in shape chicks seemed to dig me but whenever I took a shower strands of hair gathered at the drain at first I hoped it was something temporary but in time I knew just like Pa I was going bald Frank had a thick head of dark hair he got from Ma's side like the girls and Peter had curly red hair we don't know where that came from but Ma said there were red-headed cousins in Italy my hair was always thin and I was afraid I was the one to get the bald genes from Pa he was bald except for a narrow strip on each side of his scalp when Ma brought us to roust him out of some bar I found him by spotting the bald head shining in

the bar-room lights then he would get so mad to
see us all there he would tear up the house when
he got home and yell and scream in the middle of
the night for months Audry teased me acted
friendly and smiled a lot when I did my social
rounds around the store in display there was a
lot of time in between things when there wasn't
much to do I wandered the store talking with
everybody tried to time my coffee breaks around
Audry's but she always sat at a busy table in the
coffee shop so I could never get her alone the
marking room people worked different hours I
knew she took the Mass. Ave. bus and lived in
Arlington Heights but she got off a half hour
before me I liked hanging out at strip bars mostly I could sip a drink for over an hour and I never
talked with any of the girls more than a drink or
two cause it could get costly there was this beautiful young black chick used to work the clubs I
always liked watching her show she had the
tightest body I've ever seen from standing she
could lean backwards all the way until she put
her hands out flat on the floor and walk upside
down like a crab with a gorgeous shaved purple
lip pussy she got to recognize me and hit me up
for drinks if she knew I had the cash she called

herself Sugar wouldn't tell me her real name if I
bought her a second drink she might let me
touch her pussy under the table that clit of hers
stood up rock hard I can still feel it between my
fingers and think of it when I jerk off it took for
ever to get over Laura but a chick like Sugar
helped things started to come alive again I could
eat drink jerk off shit and this new chick who
worked in the coffee shop was looking real good
she was tall and for some reason wore wigs no
matter when I was with her she always had a
blond wig on she liked to fuck and party a lot
she had pretty blue eyes soft skin Sandy from
Alabama had a real strong accent I couldn't
understand her half the time she said her last job
in Alabama was a chicken chaser she was the one
who chased the chickens around the coop and
put them in a sack for the butchers we went out
for a few drinks and ended up fucking all night
at my apartment she lived with her aunt on
Summer Street turns out she was married her
husband was in jail in Alabama she had a kid
and her husband's parents had the kid she drank
every drop of cum and even licked it off of her
hands when she did me then I found out she was
fucking Billy Grimes in maintenance I liked Billy

but he was a little sleazy the last night I dropped her off she blew me right in front of her aunt's house on Summer Street with cars passing by and people walking on the sidewalk after that I put an end to it who knows who else she was doing but she didn't stay very long anyway and moved back to Alabama I still had the hots for Audry and just when I thought she was never going to have anything to do with me one day I was sitting on the parking lot wall eating a sandwich and she came out said hello lit up a smoke and sat down next to me it was the first time in almost a year since she had coffee with me alone we made some small talk and finally I said look let's cut through the crap Audry you know I'm crazy about you why won't you go out with me and she said you haven't asked me yet I told her I sure had asked her she said asking someone if they want to fool around is not the same as asking them out and she had a point in time I got real good at display there was nothing I couldn't build big or small Joe Letto had a real flair for dressing and we won awards like division of the month and employees of the month but I still wanted to get out on the sales floor with the big-ticket guys they were the ones who made the real

money and all of them wore nice suits and
owned houses and drove fancy cars and Nick
Luciano had a boat and Tony Deluca had a
horse and Mike Cordano had a beautiful house
with a built-in pool and Charlie Fresno made a
lot but he was divorced and spent every penny
paying alimony and gambling it doesn't matter
how much I make he said I never have anything I
knew no matter how long I worked in display
even with raises I couldn't make as much as
those guys and be able to take care of my family
right ever since we were kids I tried to talk Frank
out of the stupid things we could be walking
down the street and Frank suddenly decided that
he was going to climb the side of a building and
start climbing if a car was left running Frank
hopped in and drove off one time we went to a
jewelry store when I wanted to buy Ma a
bracelet from all of us on her birthday while the
salesman showed me different things Frank stole
a bunch of rings I never saw him do it when we
left he pulled the stuff out of his pocket he told
me they were for one of the neighborhood girls
who was my age he was making out with her and
feeling her up he told me that she wanted to
make out with me too one day we were alone in

her yard she said that she would show me her
pee thing if I would show her mine I was just
starting to get hair and all scared but I did anyway she ran into her house and told her mother
her mother told Ma who beat me with a broomstick like she did the time she caught me looking
under the table when I was little trying to see up
the dresses of my aunts I thought women had a
penis and the only difference between us was
that women had tits Ma pulled me out from
under there hitting me with the broomstick saying I was dirty Ma did her best but sometimes
during the week things got real lean she made
soup out of a bone or spaghetti with garlic and
oil and that's what we lived on I did good in
school but I liked working with my hands especially with wood I liked the feel of all the different grains and texture when I first took
woodworking in junior high and built a wooden
matchbox to hang on the wall mine was better
than anyone in the class Ma hung it in the
kitchen old Mr Peck the junior high woodworking teacher said I could take woodworking in the
Voke instead of going to the regular high school
I loved those shop weeks in high school cause no
matter what you were doing you had some space

around you in regular classes having to sit in one
place all day drove me crazy my mind wandered
different girls in my class then I'd get a hard-on
and pull my shirt out because you never knew
when a teacher would call you up to the black-
board I didn't want to get caught with a boner in
high school we took our regular classes with
high school kids I hated regular classes but I
could check out the girls in shop it was only guys
Mr Nunziato was the shop teacher a lot of the
guys goofed off he was always breaking up some
kind of fight for the most part I didn't get into
any trouble Mr Nunziato said I was a natural
with my hands if I stuck with it I'd do good for
my graduation project I made Ma a dresser out
of oak and surprised her with it she cried that I
could make it out of my own two hands when
we were kids and Frank first started getting me
to do him I was curious because I was feeling
these strange things down there too I don't
remember how old I was but he guided me and
told me to put it in my mouth and suck it at first
I sucked it too hard easy he said when he came in
my mouth it scared the shit out me I had no idea
what it was and spit it all over it only happened
for a few months then I told him no more there

was a guy who washed out of basic training the guys said was queer I didn't know him good Frank couldn't be queer he was just a little fucked up he always had a girlfriend but nothing would surprise me about Frank who knows it was not too long after I stopped with Frank I started jerking off after the day Audry came out to the parking lot to talk to me we finally went out for Chinese food in Chinatown she loved Chinese food too I thought that was a good sign she drank a beer and I had bourbon and cokes by the end of the second one I started to feel it and warm up Audry was cool not in a beatnik way but with her feelings you had a hard time telling what she was thinking but we talked a lot that night and got along good most of the talk was about work and gossip then she said one of the reasons she didn't like to go out with anyone she worked with was you end up talking about work all the time so we made a vow not to talk about work and I told her a little bit about the Corps and she laughed cause her ex-husband was a lifer in the army a sergeant and that got her talking about her marriage she wasn't married long the dude was real strange and old fashioned never let them see each other naked Audry

could never change in front of him they only had
sex in the dark and he didn't go for nothing but
getting on and off after two years she left him
there was a lot of problems going on with them
he wanted to have kids and she wasn't getting
pregnant he smacked her a few times and that
was the final straw after dinner we went to a bar
downtown for another drink by then I was
telling her I was burning for her she said she
wasn't a one night stand and she knew all I was
looking for was sex so why didn't I go have it
with someone else I tried to get her to come
home with me she wouldn't in front of her house
we went into a liplock that must have lasted
twenty minutes when we were finished she let
out this loud sigh like an engine releasing all the
pressure I could feel her trembling in my arms
we made out for a while and I started feeling her
up her breasts were so perfect and hard after a
few minutes grunting and groaning in the car she
said come up why don't you just come up and I
did we never left each other after that it seemed
natural to be together I loved taking drives especially alone it was one of the only things I know
calms me down I never drove until I was in the
Marines so when I got home and settled at

Pratt's I bought myself a used car when I was feeling anxious or nervous I just took a long ride it happened a lot at night cause I had trouble sleeping I could sleep for three or four hours then wake up my mind would race around so anxious I'd go out and take a walk when I was a kid many nights I went out in the middle of the night nobody ever knew I was gone there's something about how quiet the night is like the dark and the electric lights are like a man and woman right after sex when they lay there in the quiet and it's still sometimes Audry and me took long rides after we got married but a lot of times I went alone up to New Hampshire turned around and drove back it gave me time to think and was better than tossing and turning in bed with my mind running after dinner at Ma's on Sunday in the summer I drove down to Cape Cod and got out of the car to look at the ocean at night it was incredible if there was a good moon or a lot of stars the ocean just pounding in I stood there for a few minutes then turned around and drove back to the Porter Street apartment if I got horny I could just jerk off as I drove down the highway it was easier than you think with no cars on the road in the middle of the night I just kept a goo-rag under the seat strange being out on the highway doing yourself at sixty miles an hour I knew a chick who used to do herself on the road in daylight she'd wear a short summer dress with no panties when truckers drove by she'd flash them and finger her pussy for them one night when we were at her place doing it she ran out into the hall of her apartment building and started fingering herself on top of the stairs I had to drag her back in crazy thing was she never could come when she was having sex with me she said she never came with any guy she could only come when she was doing herself she was one of those clingy chicks I met her through Danny she was a friend of one of his girlfriends when I wanted to break it off with her she made a lot of crazy scenes and kept calling the apartment and sending long letters she was religious too wanted me to go to church on Sundays I guess you have to believe in God otherwise what do you believe in that doesn't mean that I go along with everything about the church and rules I liked the smell of incense and lighting candles all the colors inside the church and praying when Ma took us to the Italian mass in the North End all the old Italian widows wearing black saying the mass along with the priest in Italian smell of garlic from the old ladies' breaths some of them did their own kind of voodoo when I had a stomach ache my mother would sing the worms away making weird sounds and moving her hands over my stomach once I had a bad ear ache my mother's friend Filomena brought over some fresh breast milk in a tiny bottle she got from her daughter Ma dropped some in my ear and sang these songs Filomena said it worked better if the nipple is in the ear and the milk was fresh squeezed when Audry was pregnant her tits got milky I could gently squeeze her nipple and milk would come out she liked it when I did her pregnant said she was real horny for a few months we did it a lot and her whole body changed her pussy got wider and her tits swelled up over her belly which grew by the day she didn't like it if I sucked too much on her nipples she didn't think it was right that I should get off on sucking out the milk it didn't bother me at all but then after little Tony she wouldn't let me near her for about three months and after that even when she did sex was never the same between us Audry didn't get into doing it the way she did before the baby she liked to leave the television on for light and sometimes when I was doing her I could see her watching the screen out of the corner of her eye it bothered me but I never said nothing by the time Gina was pregnant I knew she married a loser she married him too quick after four months going with him he was one of the managers in the insurance company and made good money but he had a kid and a wife to support from another marriage he treated Gina like shit from the beginning I don't know why she wanted a guy like that I tried to talk some sense into her she wouldn't listen it was her life she said after the baby came he started hitting her she didn't have to tell us but I knew when she wasn't coming around much any more and stopped calling I dropped by her place one night she had black and blues on her arms I made her pack right then and took her and the baby to Ma's he came there a little while later I stood on the porch and told him I'd beat him to death if he came near the house but Gina went back to him and left him again a few times before he finally took off with a young chick to California she quit her job because she couldn't face the people there so I moved her and the baby in with Ma that first

week Audry and me were together we had an
intense seven days and nights I dug her and
maybe even loved her but she wanted some kind
of commitment from me when I told her I wasn't
ready for a commitment she said she wouldn't
see me any more she didn't want to be another
one of the chicks on my list even though I told
her she was more than that so we didn't see each
other for a week and avoided each other at work
then one night I came home from work there was
a card from her in the mail and it said I do my
thing you do your thing and if by chance we find
each other it's beautiful I'll always remember it
that was really important to me I still have that
card I called her and we saw each other that
night and stayed together a few weeks later
Audry gave her notice at Pratt's to take a job at
Tags in Porter Square we didn't want to be part
of the gossip circle of the store since we were living together and people did talk the day she
started at Tags she told me she was pregnant
which blew my mind cause I thought she was on
the pill she said she was on the pill but went off
it for a short time cause her doctor told her to
she wanted to know what we should do there
was nothing we could do but get married she

said she could get an abortion but there's no way that was ok with me she was worried that I would feel trapped I told her I didn't though deep inside I did but I loved Audry our sex was great and when we were together we talked about everything and it felt real easy and right I knew I wanted to get married and have kids some day but I was afraid too cause it would mean a lot of changes if I married Audry I could never do another woman again never how the fuck is someone supposed to only have sex with one person for the rest of their lives that's what I wanted to know I had been at Pratt's long enough that I had a little money built up in my profit sharing that I could borrow against it was- n't much but with that I put a small deposit down on a beat-up three-decker on Broadway in East Somerville with Audry pregnant I didn't want her to work though she said she would I believe some in all of this new women's libera- tion but I wanted my wife at home with the chil- dren I wasn't against women working or anything and even at the store there were lady managers coming in who just graduated college black managers too hey more power to them then they starting to give commission sales jobs to these chicks who were only working there a short time I told Mr Sanford I was with the store for eight years and for three I was asking to go out on the floor and sell big ticket I should have a chance too but all I'm saying is if a woman's going to marry and have children her place is in the home that was always ok with Audry for the most part she's really old fashioned later when I got into sales she always had my suits laid out for me in the morning and my shoes shined the house on Broadway needed a lot of work Audry and me moved in on the top floor my mother and the girls and Peter moved in on the second floor and I rented out the first floor to a nice Mexican couple the wife worked at the store she was hot too and before I met Audry or she met her husband once Carmen and me made out when I drove her home from having drinks but nothing ever came of it and we never said anything to each other after she moved in they paid their rent on time and I let Ma and Peter and the girls live free they just had to pay the utilities and I started fixing the place up in my spare time tearing down walls replacing windows refinishing floors replacing and hanging doors plastering ceilings painting it never ended day in and

day out but once I was out on the sales floor I
wasn't able to use my hands any more so I liked
doing that kind of work at home with Ma and
the family taken care of Frank was living with a
woman in East Boston but was beginning to
hound me to throw the people in the first floor
out so he could move in with her but I wouldn't
Gina's girl was already walking when I was starting in the vacuum-cleaner department where Mr
Sanford said I would have to prove myself before
I could consider working with the big boys in
major appliances I always thought when I fell in
love with the right woman that it would be easy
to not fool around but after Audry and me were
together for a while and then after little Tony
came we had a lot less sex before Tony came it
was pretty good but Audry was on the conserva-
tive side I was always trying to do different
things and she mostly just liked me to eat her
and get on top which was fine some of the time
but Christ those chicks in Korea some of the
things they could do I never dreamed of and I
thought I'd seen it all but Audry didn't like to
talk much about that kind of sex let alone do it
after little Tony there seemed to be no time he
was up all night or part of the night or she was

tired or something but I still jerked off I liked
jerking off in the shower best but it was hard to
find time and privacy and little Tony was up crying during the night or sick sometimes I would
take a drive but Audry didn't like it when I went
out in the middle of the night within two
months I was the top salesman in the vacuum-
cleaner department there were three of us me
and Bernie Cohen and Faith Cameron Bernie
was the strangest dude he had been working in
vacuum cleaners for twenty years never moved
on like most to major appliances or televisions
or furniture those guys would eat me alive he
said he made a decent living was never top man
but never bottom man he was a little spaced out
and a lot of the guys made fun of him he had
some kind of weird thing going on where he
would fall asleep in the middle of the day everyone who had been working in the store for a
while had their Bernie stories how once he fell
asleep leaning on an upright vacuum in the middle of the sales floor or the morning he was late
and someone spotted him in the parking lot
asleep at the steering wheel of his car there were
a number of times I remember him falling asleep
in the bathroom he used to say Tony I'm going

to the bathroom in case I'm not back in ten minutes check on me and I would and he'd be asleep on the toilet Faith was hot and I always wanted to do her but she was seeing Carl Pratt the manager of hardware who was married she was five or six years older than me and worked in the customer service department until they decided to put women out on the big-ticket sales floor we started in vacuum cleaners about the same time she had a great body big tits and it's not that I'm a tit man I like them every shape and size but she had beautiful tits and real nice legs and could wear them short skirts even though she was a little older she was a tough cookie on the sales floor and gave Bernie a run for his money I never took a coffee break though I had to be off the floor for lunch or dinner but I was back in my position on the minute I was allowed and I concentrated on nothing but selling I treated every customer with the same enthusiasm it didn't matter whether they were just looking or there to buy I would often pick up people that Bernie had let go because he didn't think they were interested and then I would sell them it drove Bernie crazy and the guys in major appliances picked up on it cause I was breaking records for

sales in the department and they started harass-
ing me that was when I really started learning
the art of needling with those guys they were
masters all they did was needle each other and
try to psyche the other guy out and they enjoyed
their arguments in front of customers so they
started coming around and watching me with
customers or when they saw me ring up another
sale they'd pass through and say nice another
one pretty soon you'll be down with the big boys
I told them you better believe I wanted in and
had every intention of working in major appliances in vacuums I started making more money
than I ever had before in one week I could make
what I was making in two weeks in display just
from selling vacuums so I started putting half
my earnings in a savings account every week and
the rest was enough to keep up the household
but I was restless I loved Audry and little Tony
and when I got home from work Audry had dinner ready and I could play with little Tony and
Ma was downstairs with the girls and Peter and I
never saw Ma so happy she could finally take it
easy and get the rest she deserved some days
when Faith wore her short skirts and her heels to
work she'd drive me crazy and all I could think

of was doing her and I would have to block it out of my mind so I could concentrate on selling but I couldn't wait to get home and do Audry but sometimes she wasn't in the mood or little Tony would be restless and I would go into the bathroom and jerk off thinking of Faith once I made the mistake of telling Audry that I still jerked off and she got all mad and jealous like and said that was an insult to her I said that everybody masturbates and she said that she didn't but I'm not sure if I believed her so I had to keep it to myself and be careful around the house most of the time I did it in the basement where I hid some magazines Jimmy out on the loading dock gave me Audry was so jealous that she drove me crazy she said she knew how I was at the store and my reputation and all so I stopped going out after work for drinks and I didn't go to any more store parties I told Audry she should just go with me to the parties if she didn't trust me but she said that she didn't want to go and if I wanted to go I should but I knew she didn't mean it I could tell by now it was clear I was going bald and with the standing around most of the day in the vacuum-cleaner department I wasn't getting much exercise at work and Audry always cooked

a big meal when I got home when I had a dinner
hour on an evening shift I drove home and she
fed me Ma taught her how to make a real gravy
and meatballs so on Sundays we all ate together
I was eating a lot and putting on weight between
the job and the projects around the house I
stopped doing my push-ups and sit-ups and for
the first time I didn't feel like I was looking good
any more Audry said she thought I was hand-
some as ever and every morning she shined my
shoes put my suit out for me and after only a
year they put me and Faith in major appliances
and it turned that division upside down because
Faith was the first time they had a woman work
in major appliances in the Cambridge store and
here's this nice looking chick among a pack of
wolves which kind of made the move over a little
easier for me since I was at least a guy but the
guys worked to keep us new ones out of the pack
Ma was always a screamer she screamed at us
kids when we were causing a fuss she screamed
at my father she screamed at God and called
upon the apostles and all the saints like they
were right there overhead but when she started
losing her sight she got quieter this is the way
God wants it first he gave me your father and

then he takes away my eyes he must be testing me she said in Italian Ma never learned much English she was able to say a few words here and there from hearing it around but if you spoke to her in English she could not understand though Frank and Gina said that she understood a lot more than we thought she did maybe she did when Audry's youngest sister came to stay with us and she heard her swearing and talking back to me and Audry she said she never heard such disrespect Sue just turned nineteen and was having trouble at home so Audry's mother and sisters thought maybe some time north would help her get it together she was a little tease walking around the apartment in a t-shirt with panties and no bra she knew she was getting me hot I could tell by the way she sat and looked at me and walked through the room she was picking up on me picking up on her she didn't look anything like Audry except for that tight body perfect ass nice firm on the small side tits her face was different and she was a natural blonde she got from her father she and Audry had different fathers I never knew Sue's father and I never knew Audry's father neither he was out of the picture by the time we met but I couldn't stand

Audry's mother if ever there was a cunt she did everything she could to control her daughters and really fucked up Audry and how she saw men because her mother hated men and was always trashing men she was married and divorced three fucking times and of course it was always the guy's fault she didn't trust anybody and that must be where Audry got her thing about trust always being suspicious and jealous I guess I'm an excitable guy it's only when other people point it out that I'm aware I wave my hands and move my body when I'm talking my voice gets louder and more excited when I was selling I used this to my advantage in vacuum cleaners I would gather a crowd around me by throwing down dirt and cigarette butts and anything else that would catch someone's eye and demonstrating the new canister with the beater bar and I would point out the trash on the floor vibrating in its path it beats it sweeps it gets out the deep down dirt I told them and to show how strong the new plastic canister was I jumped up and down on the canister several times with all my weight and I'm a hundred and eighty pounds I'd say and sometimes someone who had no intention of buying a vacuum cleaner that day

bought one and bought top-of-the-line selling
one unit was a good day's pay in commission I
was selling two and three a day with service policies which we had to sell one of the conditions
of staying in big-ticket sales was having to sell
top-of-the line and sell service policies when
they advertised a vacuum cleaner for eighty-nine
dollars we were not supposed to sell any of them
too many in one month or not enough service
policies sold in one month and you were on the
carpet with the division manager two months in
a row you were on the carpet with the hard line
manager I never sold the advertised items and I
sold service policies I started selling double and
triple service policies when I was in major appliances all the guys got on my back about it
because they said I was making them all look
bad one time we were at a regional sales meeting
for people who worked vacuum cleaners in all
the stores in eastern Massachusetts and I gave a
demonstration of how I start getting a crowd
gathered and once I got their attention I went
through all the steps and the final thing from the
first bit of dirt I threw on the floor to jumping
up and down on the canister was always letting
some lady vacuum the stuff up herself so after

all my work there was a regular person like
everyone else in the circle vacuuming up the mess
and smiling and I'd be waving my arms around
to the other people with my voice in a fever pitch
saying look at that how easy it is what a machine
and it never failed I always sold at least one I figured I was only going to make the big money if I
didn't wait for the customers to come to me all
the salesmen in the audience cheered and gave
me a standing ovation after I was finished and
when I got into major appliances I kept my cool
and never got into any of the fighting no matter
how hard they tried to piss me off I had my temper but was more likely going to yell at home
when me and Audry were in a fight or I was
arguing with Frank after the couple on the first
floor moved out I decided put a wall up in a big
room and make two smaller bedrooms and
Frank was over hounding me about taking the
apartment he had a job at the Winter Hill Tavern
as a cook and was keeping away from gambling
and he wanted to move in there with his girlfriend who was a waitress at the tavern and said
he would pay his rent on time and when I told
him no we got into an argument he said I never
gave a shit about him I told him he treated me

and the rest of the family like shit ever since I could remember Ma came down crying with Gina and Audry and little Tony too Frank said in front of them my own brother would leave me out on the street and I got so fucking mad I took a sledge hammer and knocked down the wall I just finished building Audry was afraid I was going to have a heart attack cause I was screaming and turning red all out of breath but I didn't stop until every bit of that wall was down a month's work down the toilet the house needed so much work outside and in no matter where I was working it seemed there was too much to do I worked nights after work and mornings if I had an evening shift at the store and on my days off even Sundays except I took a couple of hours off for dinner so all I was doing was working and coming home to the house and there was always a problem like the toilet was backed up or ceilings were leaking in the rain or the electrical system would fail cause it had to be updated no matter how many times I told everyone not to use all the things at once they still used too many things and finally Gina would turn on her hairdryer and blow a circuit and I blew my top it was great to see little Tony growing but Audry seemed sad and said she wanted to have another baby so she got pregnant with Johnny by the time Johnny came everything seemed to be at its worst with the house all the work I did you could hardly notice I finally let Frank move in the first floor which was the only finished apartment for the first few months he paid his rent on time but in a matter of a few weeks he was having huge fights with his girlfriend they both worked nights and drank after work and didn't get home until one or two in the morning they would argue and keep us all up she would yell out things like I hate your fucking guts and he would call her a bitch and a cunt I tried to talk with him he said keep out of it one night he started hitting her I went down there and told him if it happened again I would call the cops and I meant it that's when he ended up fighting with her out in the street and took out his pistol and shot it in the air it made a hole over the front door the hole was there for ever I went down out of my mind we fought in the street I wasn't in the shape I was when I got back from the Marines but I was crazy enough with anger that nothing Frank did could stop me I ran down and beat the shit out of him I beat him bloody and

his girlfriend was screaming at me to stop and by
now Ma and the girls and Audry too all screaming the cops came and took Frank down the station and confiscated his gun they took me too
we spent a couple of hours at the station and
since no one wanted to press charges they
charged Frank with shooting a gun or something
and if he pleaded guilty they reduced it so he got
probation he begged me not to put him out he
had no place to go and his girlfriend moved out
so he could only pay me half the rent I let him
stay on the condition that if he violated his probation he was out and he said ok Audry didn't
like Frank and she told me right out there was
something about him that gave her the creeps
and I have to agree even though he is my brother
Frank's a fucked-up dude Audry's mother and
sisters kept hounding her to take the kids and go
down and visit but Audry came up with different
excuses why she couldn't go but the real reason
was she didn't trust me and she didn't want to
leave me alone for any length of time she
watched me like a hawk if I didn't go home for
lunch she asked who I ate lunch with and one
day a week when I worked evening shift a bunch
of us went out for supper across the street at

Iagos or for Chinese food it drove her crazy if
any of the girls from the store went along and
though Audry never came right out and asked
me to the point about anything she had a way of
questioning in this slow and round-about way to
find out exactly where I went out on errands or
who I spent time with at work I had no friends
since Danny moved out to San Francisco and I
didn't hear from him no more at work I still flirted with all the chicks I could but I drew the line
and didn't go out after work with anyone and
didn't fool around since Audry and me had been
together I was either at the store home doing
work on the house or out getting supplies I needed for the house work Audry was busy with little
Tony and Johnny and shit before you know it
Johnny is five and already starting school at the
store I was mostly first or second in sales every
month I sold the most top-of-the-line merchandise which meant commission and a spiff a spiff
was a bonus sometimes twenty or thirty dollars
on top of the commission I had the highest service policy sales in the region the managers loved
me and the guys hated me by now there had been
so much fighting in major appliances over customers that a timer bell was put in each one of

us got five minutes on the point when the bell
went off the next in line got the point for five
minutes and so on and made the amount of customers distributed better but I still outsold
everyone most of the time the guys made
remarks about me living in Somerville in a three-
decker house and my beat-up car when I drove it
into the ground and bought a little Japanese
thing it gave them something to rib me about
they drove Caddies and Rivieras and big
Oldsmobiles and always wanted to know what I
was doing with all my money maybe hoarding it
away not spending it on a house or car that's for
sure but when I was at work I never lost it I concentrated on nothing but selling sure there were
chicks around and that could distract me especially at that time in Cambridge all these hippie
chicks coming into the store no bras and mini-
skirts I had all I could do to keep it in my pants
and when Audry took her first visit down to see
her mother and sisters she took the boys with
her and one of the nights I decided to go out by
myself to the Zone  and went to a movie and a
bar to watch some shows like I used to do before
I was married and in one of the joints there was
a gorgeous young blonde and I spent over a hun-

dred dollars buying her drinks and she rubbed
me and said she sometimes saw guys on her off
hours let me tell you that was the fucking test
but I went home and jerked off about five times
and when Audry got back she seemed anxious
for me to do her so I did and we had great sex
but over the next couple of weeks we argued a
lot because in her way of being kind of passive
she was trying to find out my every move during
her trip if she caught wind that I went to the
Zone it would have really made trouble we
talked on the phone every day she was away and
even then I could sense her on the other end trying to figure things out when me and her were
having sex Audry never liked giving me head
even when she did and it wasn't very often it was
obvious that she wasn't into it so it kind of
ruined it for me I always asked the girls in the
bars the same questions like how long they'd
been a stripper and where did she come from
how old was she did her parents know what she
did cause I think of that sometimes if I had a
daughter what would I do if she was doing this
and I always was interested in people and finding
out about how they think and why they think
that way I liked the shops in the Zone best all the

books and magazines shelves of vibrators and
dildos and double-ended dildos it's another
world I always asked Audry was there anything
special she would like me to do to her but she
didn't like to talk about those things she'd think
I went crazy if I ever tried to use a vibrator or a
dildo on her Frank's new girlfriend loved it when
he pulled out his box of toys he had something
for every hole he said that was the same girlfriend he used to piss on they used to go into the
shower and turn the shower on and then Frank
would piss on her and she would get off he said
she loved it shit I couldn't even get Audry to
blow me and Frank's pissing on chicks in the
shower downstairs when I was having the house
done over with aluminum siding Frank got in
way over his head with the bookies he borrowed
from a loanshark to pay the bookies figuring he
could gamble his way out of it but it got worse
and he needed ten thousand dollars fast he said I
was his only hope or he was going to be in serious trouble with some bad people I gave him the
ten thousand then threw the workers off of the
job they only finished three sides of the house
with the yellow siding but I left the fourth side
which was the one you could see from both

streets cause it was a corner house unfinished
with the old tarpaper shingling to serve as a
daily reminder to Frank Audry pleaded with me
to finish the job but I left it and Frank stopped
paying rent again but was being friendly and had
some movies he wanted me to see they were
mostly orgy movies with everyone fucking and
sucking each other Audry thought it was all dis-
gusting but later that night she wanted me to do
her and she told me that when she was bringing
some trash down she could see part of the movie
screen in Frank's apartment because the kitchen
door was part open and she watched for a few
minutes and it got her real hot we did it two or
three times that night I thought we made a
breakthrough but the next day it was like it never
happened when I brought it up she hushed me
up and said she didn't want to talk about that
stuff with the kids around the boys were great
and good kids too little Tony was the goofy and
noisy one and Johnny was the quiet one I never
went in for sports and that stuff but I figure you
should do that with your sons so I took them
both to the sporting goods store and bought new
gloves and bats and balls a few times we went
over to Foss Park and hit the ball around but I

wasn't too good at it and the boys didn't seem to be all that interested I took them to Fenway Park to see the Red Sox play Johnny liked it ok but Tony didn't I never watched sports like most guys mostly I didn't watch much television it wasn't that I didn't like it but I was always doing something Audry had it on all the time she watched those soap operas in the afternoon it was the same old stuff who was doing who just like at the store the only one who wasn't doing anybody was me except for Audry and that was only once in a while even though Audry denied it she only did it to make me happy most of the time she never even got off but at least she didn't fake it that would have been worse Ma belonged to one of the religious societies in the North End so we always went to the feast from the time we were little kids and I used to take Ma and Audry and the boys on Sundays during the summer the boys enjoyed it and ran around the streets and Ma sat in with all her old lady friends from her religious society most of them widows wearing all black Audry and me went around and ate I loved the quahogs raw but it made Audry sick the sight of those things sitting there on the shell I would throw down a buck and suck back a

handful each of them like the pussy of Venus
and we always got sausage and pepper sand-
wiches and Italian ice when we were kids Frank
and me carried the blanket behind the statue of
the saint in the parade people would pin bills
right on to the statue and the parade would stop
while they lifted up a cute little girl to pin a dollar bill on the statue of Saint Anthony and the
blanket was so you could toss change into it
from the sidewalk or above where people hung
out windows Frank would steal change from the
blanket when no one was looking one day he
made ten dollars there were always some hot
looking chicks running around and Audry would
get pissed when she'd catch me checking one out
and she'd want to go home then we'd get into a
fight driving on the way home and I'd threaten
to drive the car off the road with everybody in it
and Audry said that was a nice thing to say in
front of the boys the thing about Audry was she
really hated going out of the house she made me
the grocery list and I did the shopping she had
no friends though I didn't neither but even when
I wanted to go out to the beach or the zoo or
somewhere she never wanted to go and lots of
times she would say why don't I take the boys

and go and sometimes me and the boys would go out alone Audry liked to do the housework and watch television mostly and besides that she talked to her sisters and her mother in North Carolina on the phone the phone bill was through the roof most of the time but it was her only thing she really spent money on so I didn't say much about it except if she talked too much when I was home because it drove me crazy the gossip and shit and which one of her sisters was breaking up with who it would go on and on finally I would tell her get off the phone and talk with her family when I was at work when I got my ten-year pin I was the top salesman in major appliances and the number-one salesman in big ticket throughout the district of eight stores and I never let up so that year in and year out everyone knew I would come out on top the fight now was for who would be behind me in second I made more money than I ever dreamed of but I was starting to get bored while I could sell top-of-the-line and service policies in my sleep it was taking more energy out of me cause I had to fight my boredom I was bored at home the boys were growing and had their own friends and Audry and me seemed to disagree about any-

thing if the sun was shining and I said nice day
she would say no it isn't and it just got to be this
constant kind of bickering even though I loved
her more than I could love any other woman she
had my children and was a great mother a great
wife and would never refuse sex but it's not that
she wouldn't refuse sex but that she wasn't really
into it Josie got married to a great guy who was
an accountant and Peter moved out and got his
own place in Medford and Gina was seeing this
guy off and on but he was a loser and it wasn't
working out but her daughter Maria was as
beautiful as she was and smart too Frank had
stopped paying any rent for a couple of years so
I carried the nut on the whole house but I bought
it cheap and as the years passed it seemed like
less and less so I was still able to save a lot of
money and looking to pay off the house completely they had to make me take my vacations
at Pratt's I had so much built up so when I took
time off I mostly stayed home and worked on the
house Audry never wanted to do much sometimes in the summer we might go to the beach or
I'd take the boys over the Foss Park pool but
Audry would stay home one thing I can say
about her she kept the place immaculate Ma

would be proud if she could only see cause Ma
always said that any woman who couldn't keep
her house clean was not a woman you wanted to
be married to but mostly during that time she sat
at the front window all day and we checked in on
her the boys would always visit her but she sat
quiet by the window it was the strangest thing
for me watching Ma get old and quiet said she
was waiting for her time God was going to call
her soon she would be ready she was still healthy
and except for her eyes the doctor told her she
had a long time to go before she was ready to go
to God but she said she knew that God did what
he wanted to do not what the doctor said and
she wanted to be ready when it was time on
Sundays we walked her to church she never
missed one Sunday at mass I took communion
with her when we were young and when she took
to sitting at the window all day she had her
rosary beads in her hand and said the rosary in
Italian when me and Audry did talk about going
away somewhere she only wanted to go visit her
family in North Carolina there was no way I was
going down and stay with her mother and sisters
for a week I told her she could go herself and
sometimes she did it was fine for me I got a little

time alone at home and snuck out to the Zone
for an evening but no matter how close I came
and how much I flirted I always stopped short of
fooling around I wanted to go to New York City
for a vacation that was the last place she would
go but one time after I hounded her and then got
real quiet for a long time after she said she
would go with me it was the first time we were
together without the boys we left them with
Gina for the weekend and stayed at a nice hotel
but we didn't do a fucking thing because Audry
wouldn't leave the room she was afraid we
would get mugged and said we shouldn't go out
walking the streets of New York if we didn't
know our way around I wanted to go out and
have dinner and walk through Times Square I
mean just the energy in that city it's all sex it's
the only place I've ever been where I get a hard-
on just walking down the street so we got room
service the first night and the second night I told
Audry that I wasn't staying in the room again
and we had a fight so I just went out myself and
had a ball they got live sex shows and people
come out and fuck right in front of you I went to
peep shows and live shows and porn shops and
talked with strangers on the street it was like this

high I didn't get back until six in the morning
Audry was up and had our bags packed we left
and fought the whole ride back to Boston somehow that trip to New York was when things really started going bad for us of all my family
members I worried about Peter the most he was
always lost even though he had his own apartment in Medford he spent a lot of his spare time
at Ma's and she cooked for him and sent him
home with food amazing Ma the way she could
still find her way around the kitchen and cook
being blind Peter wanted more than anything to
get married but I knew it would take a special
girl to marry Peter he wasn't the best looking
guy and wore his glasses and a hearing aid and
speech defect because he was hard of hearing he
was a tall guy with curly red hair gentle like a little kid except if he drank so he didn't drink too
much once and a while if he got too drunk he'd
show up at Ma's and start yelling about how bad
his life was I had to calm him down and drive
him home he cried sometimes and said I don't
know what it's like to be alone I have Audry and
the boys he'll always be alone and never have a
family who would want him I told him marriage
isn't all it's supposed to be and if I had to do it

over as much as I love Audry and the boys I
would stay single and he should stay single he's
not missing as much as he thinks there was plenty of whoring he could do if he quit feeling sorry
for himself sex had nothing to do with how you
look it had to do with your attitude some of the
most ugly chicks can be sexier than the prettiest
chicks if you ask me and there would be plenty
of chicks who might be interested in him in the
meantime he could always pay for it there was
nothing wrong with that but he believed that
kind of thing wasn't right there was something
to what he said that was true about having a wife
and kids because as hard as it was having kids no
matter how it changed everything with me and
Audry that connection I had with the boys was
hard to describe but not like anything else little
Tony was heavy and we tried to keep an eye on
his eating cause he always ate too much if you
didn't stop him or he would go into the cabinet
and eat a box of cookies so we had to be on him
as he grew older Johnny was kind of fragile he
never slept good many nights he woke up crying
and I would sit in the rocking chair in the living
room with him on my lap and rock him for
hours until he finally fell asleep sometimes we

slept there all night and he was just the opposite of little Tony once he started getting older he never wanted to eat he looked so skinny and we had to struggle with him all the time to get him to eat he was anxious and nervous and twitched his eyes which the doctor said was a nervous habit but they were good boys never got into trouble and did what I told them to do I sent them to St Ann's because I think the sister schools give them more discipline though now a lot of the teachers aren't sisters any more but they still give them the religion and the discipline which I think is important for kids with all the stuff going on around with drugs and protest too many of those kids had never been away from home and they ran around and criticized this country this is the greatest country in the world why do you think everyone wants to come here from other countries if these kids don't like it they should go to China or Russia and smarten up fucking fast when they end up working the fields all fucking day for a meal and a bed it's not I'm against the long hair and the chicks burning their bras more power to them sex and love you got it but you can't just decide you're gonna change the world overnight and expect it to hap-

pen I mean what the fuck you can do anything
you want I started out with nothing and one of
my dreams was always to have my own business
so as I got more bored at the store and was able
to save money I started looking around at different things I guess one of the things I always
thought would be a good thing to invest in was a
pizza shop it's good money a pizza cost a quarter
to make and you sold it for four dollars and I figured the boys could work after school and that
kind of thing but a lot of the guys at work said I
was crazy to do something like that I would
make less than I do now and work more hours
seven days a week Audry said that whatever I
thought was best was ok with her I had enough
built up in my profit sharing and savings to do it
I looked at a few places and they were pretty
dumpy it would use up all of our savings to do it
and if it didn't work I'd be stuck cause there's no
way to guarantee I could get my Pratt's job back
and Angelo Russo from hardware left Pratt's
after twenty years and moved his whole family
out to California to open a pizza shop out there
and did fabulous and came in the store a year
later on a visit looking tanned and said it was
the best thing he ever did and the week he got

back to California he dropped dead from a heart attack so that kind of scared me a little I took a huge life insurance policy in case something should happen to me the house would get paid off and Audry and the boys and Ma would be ok they made me take a medical exam it was the first time since I was in the Marines cause I never went to the doctor if I had a cold or a stomach bug or something I just let it work itself I knew after my five-year pin when I never called in sick that no matter how long I stayed at the store I wasn't going to call in sick when I had the physical they told me I had to get exercise and lose weight I gained thirty pounds since I left the Marines and being a short guy it looked even worse but I let myself go and I didn't eat right sometimes if I couldn't sleep I'd boil macaroni in the middle of the night and eat a bowl and go back to bed I loved ice cream and could sit down and eat a quart like nothing but the doctor told me if I didn't watch it I was going to be right on target for a heart attack so I went on this diet and Audry helped me and cooked all this diet stuff I ate a lot of salads and chicken and had to stop eating ice cream and cut down on the macaroni they said I had to stop drinking Pepsi cause

I drank about six or ten cans a day sometimes so
I switched over to sugar-free stuff and it tasted
like shit at first but after a while I got used to it I
started doing sit-ups and push-ups again it took
a while but I started to lose some pounds I wanted to lose the thirty that I gained after six
months I lost twenty Audry said I was looking
good and for a while we started having more sex
it was easier without the big belly underneath
me I had more energy and felt like a new man
and the chicks at the store were all saying I was
looking good the only thing was most of the hair
was gone from the top of my head it made me
feel real awkward about myself when I lost the
weight I had to buy some new suits cause the
others were too big then I bought another new
Toyota which cost twice as much as the first one
I bought but I was feeling good and not as bored
as I was at work and I finally had the last side of
the house sided and the three front porches done
over after all the years most of the work was
done Christ where the time goes I can't tell little
Tony was already in his first year of high school
the sex thing with Audry didn't last too long she
was jealous that chicks in the store found me
attractive and after a while we were back to our

bickering deep down I knew that she would just
as soon we sell the house pack up and move to
North Carolina cause a couple of times she said
that there was no place to get a good pizza anywhere down there it would be a great place for
me to open up a business the last fucking place I
would move would be North Carolina but her
family always came to visit us and parked themselves in the apartment for as long as they wanted that bitch mother of hers and the little tease
sister I don't know which one of them went
through more guys all they did was sit around
smoke cigarettes drink coffee and gossip they
couldn't stand me one bit so I made sure if I
could I made them uncomfortable as I could
without pissing Audry off too much it wouldn't
bother me if they never came back again after all
the work and money I put into the house all they
did was try to get Audry to move down there as
time wore on they didn't care if it was with me
or without me once when her little sister was
staying with us she said she was in the basement
bringing down trash Frank cornered her and
forced himself on her she whacked him hard
cause he had a mark on his cheek he said she
came on to him and when he tried to push her

away she hit him I believed Audry's sister though I wouldn't put coming on to Frank past her I lost my cherry cause of Frank I was twelve and he used to do his girlfriend at her house her parents weren't home during the day and one day Frank brought me along his girlfriend had a younger sister who was fourteen when Frank and his girl-friend went into the bedroom me and the sister were on the couch she asked me did I want to make out and we did it didn't take long cause she knew what she was doing she made me pull out and not come inside her years later Frank told me he was doing the little sister too after that it was a couple of years before I had sex and it was because of Frank again he fixed me up with some friend of one of his girlfriends who liked the idea of doing it with a young kid she was eighteen man did she go to town she left claw marks on my back later I used to see her around town she was a waitress at Sandy's Diner on Mass. Ave. she had a couple of kids but I think she got divorced her old man got hooked on drugs but it's the sex thing I can never figure out it's the first thing I think of when I wake up and the last thing I think of before I'm sleeping if I'm lucky I dream about it too in the course of any day at the store between the chicks who worked there and female customers I could have fucked morning noon and night and not been satisfied I wasn't getting much at home even if Audry wanted it was always the same way me eating her then getting on top I wanted to mix it up use some toys watch some flicks but Audry wouldn't and when she did go down on me she did this gagging thing like she couldn't keep it in there it's not that I was so big I wasn't it was a reflex as soon as she'd put the head in she'd start to gag and that was a turnoff but a lot of the people in the store were having a good time I had to be the only one not in on it there was Jane De Pasqulae a recent college graduate tall dark long legs and big tits who within a month of being in her position in ladies' fashions went right to the top and started fooling around with Mr Murphy the store manager and by the end of the year Jane was promoted over many more qualified people to manage the television and stereo department and May Sullivan of ladies' fashions was fooling around with Eddie Arziano the manager of automotive who was married and May never fooled around in the store before and all the younger kids were doing each other Brian Walsh the new kid in vacuums which merged with sewing machines who was married with two kids was fooling around with Diane Di Martino she worked part-time in draperies and linens who was married with three kids on and on and everybody but me I just jerked off whenever I could and flirted my ass off but you get pretty fucking tired of window-shopping Audry would be all over my ass about who I was hanging out with at work even if I wanted to fool around it would be impossible the way she kept tabs on me but she knew I flirted said I know you Tony and I know what you're capable of sometimes I used to want to just go out and do it to get back at her sometimes I would just want to do it because I wanted to do it why shouldn't people be able to take advantage of the greatest thing God gave us I could never understand but to me even if you're married if you want to have sex with someone else and they know you're married and they're just into it for the sex why not let the flame burn it's not cheating it's just sex I mean if Audry wanted to have one of those marriages it would be ok with me but she never would I wouldn't mind knowing Audry was doing some other guy as long as she loved me and things were the same way they were at home shit they'd probably be better we'd probably have more sex hey I wouldn't mind watching her or joining in there's nothing wrong with three-ways and foursomes but Audry was too hung up about that stuff I guess we all have some kind of fucked-up feelings because even though I like the idea of doing those things with Audry she's the mother of my kids so that kind of makes it a little weird but how do you put a gauge on all that stuff who's to say what's normal when Craig started working at the store part-time that Christmas season he was a floater and worked in any department that needed help except for the big-ticket departments only straight commission people worked there but he worked in sporting goods a lot which was right next to major appliances and the guys made jokes about him being a sissy and a member of Joe Letto's church he was a sweet kid but something a little wild about his eyes one day Ned Logue from hardware called him a ballerina in front of him and I could tell the kid's feelings were hurt he turned red and ran into the stock room I told Ned to back off and he said oh sure Luongo I've had your number all along Ned was getting back at me there was a blonde that

worked in the office and her and Ned used to
fool around sometimes I was doing her at the
same time and Ned wanted her all for himself
she told me that Ned told her that Danny and
me used to get it on but there's no way Ned
could have known about me and Danny so Craig
got kind of friendly with me and I got to know
him a little bit he was a frail kid feminine too but
cute in an odd sort of way dirty blond hair and
blue eyes after the Christmas season he stayed on
in the shoe department working a few nights a
week I saw less of him because shoes was
upstairs but one night when Audry and the boys
were on vacation it must have been February
because it was during a freezing spell he was out
in front of the bus stop when I was pulling out of
the parking lot and I pulled over and picked him
up he lived in Dorchester and said he didn't want
to put me out but I told him it was no problem
besides it was zero outside and quarter of ten at
night I thought he'd have to get home he could-
n't be more than seventeen but he asked me did I
want to go out for a drink and he took me to this
place in the South End called The Other Side
believe you me it was dimly lit with candles and
there were queers and guys in drag and couples

clutching in the corner shadows everyone on the make transsexuals and transvestites the guys that weren't in drag were dressed in jeans and black sweaters and leather caps and Craig knew everyone and introduced me around I couldn't believe it it was like nothing I'd seen yet and I'd been in the Marines and traveled to the Orient some of the queens were young young as my little Tony and it was hard to believe they weren't real chicks but some of them were kind of pitiful the older dudes with holes in their stockings bad make-up jobs and beat-up wigs me and Craig sat down in one of the corner booths he told me a little about his home situation his mother was dead his father was a severe alcoholic and when he was drunk he beat-up on Craig and his sister and brother Craig had spent some time on the run and lived in a half-way house he moved back home when he got the job at Pratt's and was going to take some kind of test so he could get his high-school diploma cause he dropped out when he went on the run but he was a good student when he was young but for a while he was either staying with friends or sometimes on the street he was on probation and that was why he had the job and moved back in with his father he was driving in a car with someone who had drugs they both got arrested and since it was his first offense he only got probation we talked for hours I told him about my growing up and Audry and the boys the joint seemed to be open all night and I didn't get home until four in the morning the phone was ringing when I was coming through the front door Audry was hysterical wanting to know where I'd been and saying how worried she was she called my mother Ma said I never came home from work she called the store and it was closed and she was getting ready to call the police I told her at the last minute I decided to go out for drinks with a few of the guys at work and because I was sleepy from the drinks I stopped at Mr Donuts for a coffee and a donut donuts are one of my weaknesses and before I went on my diet I would sometimes stop at Mr Donuts and pick up a half dozen and eat them while taking a drive but anyway I told her the coffee woke me up and I didn't want to go home to an empty house cause I missed her and the boys so I decided to take a ride and before I knew it I was at the New Hampshire border and on the way back I ran out of gas cause I forgot to check the tank I was out there for a long time it was below zero when finally a trooper came up and took me to a place open all night so I could get a can of gas and so that's why I was getting home so late she believed me though later she found ways to work in questions about the night to try and trick me into a mistake in my story but there was a code with most of the guys at work if you said you were out with them you were and I told Ma next time Audry called when she was away don't tell her anything Ma got more frail and lost her appetite if it's one thing she always had was a good appetite we started having to beg her to eat and I wanted to take her to the doctor for a check-up but she wouldn't go she said she was ready to go and when God wanted her she wanted to be there by then Josie had her first kid a boy and Gina's Maria was already in junior high school Peter met this woman who worked at Schrafts who was kind of odd old fashioned looking like she lived in the forties or something she was quiet and older than him and still lived with her mother and father in Roxbury and in a few months they got married they were the strangest couple don't get me wrong I love him and I took her in as my own by Jesus she was bigger than he was and had a mustache and I was best man and Frank was an usher and Josie and her daughter and Gina were bridesmaids and we got the Italian American Hall on Broadway and had a great party with a band I drank too much wine and got a little wild and led a dance around the hall waving my napkin with my shirt off except the bow-tie and Audry got all pissed and said I made a fool of myself but I had a great time besides Audry wouldn't dance with me anyway and then on Sundays Peter brought his wife Teresa over for dinner she reminded me of a nun and I couldn't imagine doing her that's saying something for me but she loved Peter he loved her and that's what counts they were trying to have a baby but it wasn't happening for some reason so they were going to the doctors for check-ups the doctors said Teresa was a little old even though she was still able to get pregnant the odds were not good Peter took it real bad he started drinking and getting into arguments with her Teresa called me on the phone and I had to go over and calm him down one time it happened she had a bruise on her face and that's when I found out he was hitting her which was so fucked up because Peter was really so gentle he was the last guy I think

that would hit his wife but when he drank he had
no control I shook him up some and told him if
it happened again he was going to deal with me
he started on one of his pity me things how bad
it's been for him everyone always made fun of
him and Pa hated him now he wasn't going to be
able to have kids then before you know it Teresa
got pregnant forty-four years old and delivered a
healthy girl they named Anna after Ma I must
say most babies are cute no matter what but
Anna was an ugly baby with this oversized head
everyone was nice about it though and said how
cute she was Frank's cigarette beer and grocery
money came from his various girlfriends as old
and fat as Frank got he always had a good looking girlfriend to live with and take care of the
bills I got tired of trying to get money out of him
what's a few hundred a month to me he said I
had plenty the house was almost paid for and
Gina didn't pay rent why should he I told him
Gina took care of Ma and she paid her utilities if
Frank didn't gamble he would have done ok he
was a good cook they liked him at the Winter
Hill Tavern and paid him good I remember a guy
in the Marines same thing it was cards with him
though Frank it was more dogs and horses and

the sports games Frank loved to watch sports if
you had a bet on the game he said it made it special somehow but this guy in the Marines most
of the guys would be out looking for pussy he
was at the card game and always owed money
soon as our pay came in every month all of his
went to everybody in the company who he owed
they say it's a disease gambling I never took to it
when I was young Frank took me to the dog
track with him he tried to show me how to han-
dicap and all that I just looked at the dogs and
chose the one I liked I did as good as Frank with
all his arithmetic and figuring things out in his
little notebook and that would piss him off most
of the time we just lost so by the time Frank was
a teenager he was already losing a lot of money
every week it's a hard habit to break I tried to
teach the boys the rights and wrongs of things
they see Frank and know about his gambling
they know how something like that can ruin
your life they heard stories about Pa from
Ma and me and Gina and Josie little Tony had
trouble in school he was a slow learner his report
cards were never good mostly Cs and Ds but he
got good marks for effort Johnny got As almost
all the time what a fit he threw when he got a B I

loved the boys more than anything it's funny
how when you have kids everything changes I
worried about things I never worried about
before and it got me to thinking more about
myself and the things about myself I wouldn't
want the boys to know like some of the sex stuff
and hanging out down the Zone but everybody
has different sides to themselves and the boys
were only human too and would have their own
things but there were things about myself I did-
n't want to see in the boys and I worried about
them being around Frank a lot him being so
crazy I never appreciated Ma more as when
those boys were growing up and I realized how
much work she had to do alone to keep the family together and deal with Pa and all his shit
beating up on her and never having any money
around how much she loved us and made sure we
had food in our stomach and understood right
from wrong and respect for certain things that's
what I tried to teach the boys and mostly we got
along good only sometimes when I lost my temper and yelled they got upset I never hit them but
sometimes if they were driving me crazy I'd yell
and threaten to burn the house down or something like that Audry would interfere and then

me and her would start arguing I guess I yelled a
lot around the house and that wasn't too good
for the boys but everybody makes mistakes raising their kids there's no perfect way to do it I
don't care who you are when Craig started missing shifts at work and not calling in or anything I
heard they gave him a warning and then the
week he got fired I talked with him and he said
things were real bad at home and his father had
been drinking a lot and hitting everybody sometimes he didn't come in because he was afraid to
leave the house cause there was no one there to
protect his brother and sister from the father but
I lost touch with him after that and often wondered what happened to him that was the summer me and Audry actually split up for a few
weeks she went to North Carolina with the boys
and I flew down there to get them back when I
first realized they left for the airport I drove
down there like a maniac and left my car out
front of a terminal and ran all over the airport
trying to find the next plane to North Carolina
when I got back the car was towed and I owed
three hundred for storage when I got down to
North Carolina I paid a hundred bucks just to
get a taxi to her mother's place all I had was an

address and we had a big scene in front of her mother's house cause Audry wouldn't come out and talk to me her mother told me from the porch I had to get off her property and little Tony and Johnny were in the upstairs window looking out and I threatened her mother I would kill her and the rest of her family if she didn't let me talk to Audry and kept me from my boys and that bitch called the cops on me and they threatened to arrest me if I didn't leave so that night I sent a telegram from my hotel to the house to Audry it said I do my thing you do your thing and if by chance we find each other it's beautiful and Audry called me at the hotel and said she was sorry for everything that happened but things were unbearable for her in the house I didn't know how hard it was to live with me I was always yelling and making threats and trying to make rules for everybody and everybody outside thought I was such a great guy but they should see me at home her words made me really angry I wanted to just go nuts having to hear that I wasn't nearly the great husband and father I thought I was on one hand and thinking Audry was full of shit and brainwashed by her mother and sisters on the other but who was the one

working his ass off all these years making the
money and working on the house so that now it
was worth something why was I all of a sudden
such an asshole all these years and she never said
nothing before she said she loved me but ever
since Ma died and I turned forty she said it was
just getting worse Ma died in her sleep but in the
end we never thought it would come for she kept
sleeping longer and longer every day until she
was sleeping over twenty hours a day eating like
a bird and shrinking away to nothing there were
days when she was in extreme pain and Gina
would beg me to call the doctor and Ma calling
from her bed in the room yelling in Italian don't
call the doctor Ma made me promise to leave it
to God and go when he wanted her that she lived
her years and did everything she was going to do
and now it was up to God in his hands she didn't
want to go to the hospital and get hooked up to
those electronic machines that keep you alive so I
kept my promise even though there were times
when Gina and Josie Peter and even Frank were
fighting with me about how to care for Ma she
should be in a hospital or nursing home call the
doctor but I gave my word to Ma and I kept it to
the end one morning Gina went in and Ma was

cold her body stiff Ma got her wish but Gina said it wasn't fair that we all had to sit around and watch her die for two years I had a nice headstone carved for her and buried in her own grave just the way she asked me to and not with Pa who was at a nearby cemetery and I went to Ma's cemetery every Sunday morning and brought flowers sometimes I brought the boys but Audry never went she said she didn't like cemeteries her family was going to get cremated when they die I told her if she died before me there was no way I was going to have her cremated she was going to have a church funeral and be buried with me in a proper grave with a headstone so Audry stayed in North Carolina she said she loved me and didn't want the marriage to break up but she needed a little time and I had to give her space I was worried about the boys and couldn't stand the idea that they were with her but they were having a good time and one of Audry's sisters had horses and the boys were learning to ride I had all I could do to not go down there kill Audry and her whole fucking family and take the boys back home with me but I wasn't on my turf down there and knew that the cops meant business so I went back home

and played it cool at work none of the guys
knew what was going on except that I had to do
my own clothes and shoes and laundry and
cooking and cleaning I talked to Audry every day
and told her I wanted her to come home she said
she wasn't ready yet and one night I was working
at the store and got a call near closing time from
Craig who said he was sorry to bother me but he
had nowhere to turn his father had thrown him
out he was in a bad way could I come down to
The Other Side and meet him so after work I
drove down the South End and when I got to the
bar I couldn't find him at first I was about to
leave when I heard him call my name and I
turned to see him in the same corner table we sat
in the first time we were there but he was in drag
and that's what threw me off I guess I should
have figured it out in the first place I mean I
knew he was queer and all but he never said anything about being a dresser he had on make-up
but his face was bruised and there was dry blood
on his lips he didn't have a wig on just his own
blond hair with these long fake diamond earrings and this long evening dress and heels I was
uncomfortable at first but once I relaxed it was
ok shit everybody in the place was ok no reason I

shouldn't be he thanked me for coming it was really nice of me and he always knew I was someone special I ordered a bourbon and coke and drink for him though he was slurring his words and I could tell he must have already had a lot he told me his father came home drunk just when he was getting ready to leave the house and when his father saw him in the dress he went crazy beat him up bad then threw him out for good there was still blood trickling from his nose he had a lump over his eye he looked at me and said I don't know what to do I feel like there's nothing left for me I said there was always things you could do but first he had to get on his feet and get a job and a place to live we finished our drinks and I took him to the Howard Johnson's Motor Lodge and got him a room for the night he could barely walk by the time we got to the room being on heels drunk so I helped him undress first I took off his shoes and earrings then his necklace and the long white gloves I leaned him up on his side unzipped him then pulled his dress down over his shoulders to his waist then over his ankles I saw him in the bra and pantyhose and realized I was digging it and I wanted him so I went to the bathroom to get a grip of myself and soaked a washcloth to wipe down my face then his face and got the dried-up blood and smeared make-up off he also had a cut on his lip I remember that's when I realized how close men and women really are and how with a little bit of imagining there wasn't much different in the way a boy or a girl looked except how they wore their hair and made up their skin and dressed it was only naked that the differences were obvious but in the face it was closest I saw him then as a chick the exact way he would have looked if he was a chick and he leaned his head back on the pillow and made a content sound like mmmmmmmm and looked at me and lifted his head to kiss me and I kissed him on the lips then he shoved his tongue down my throat and was all over me it was like nothing I ever knew in my life we went at it for hours I lost count of how many times finally about three in the morning I knew I better get home so I gave him some money to get him through a few days and told him I wanted to help him but only call me at work and I went home Audry had called the house all night I told her I went out to Chinatown then for a long drive cause I was missing her so much and feeling so down and she said Tony if I find out you're lying it's over but then she said she thought it over a long time and didn't want to let the marriage go that easy we should give it another try but some things were going to have to change the idea that she had the boys down there still made me crazy and when she said she was going to be home soon I told her I couldn't wait and how much I missed her and the boys and I was nothing without them I couldn't sleep the rest of the night the next morning on the way to work I left early and drove to the Howard Johnson's Motor Lodge but Craig was already gone I couldn't stop thinking of him and what I had done with him the night before sometimes I just told myself it never happened in time I think I could convince myself I felt sick inside in a strange sort of way because after all Craig was only a few years older than little Tony and I couldn't help but think that I was really fucked up that was the first time in my life I really felt guilty and fucked up no matter what I did in my life or what other people did my attitude was always whatever turns you on and I believed that too what difference did it make anyway whether it was a chick or a guy it was the first time ever I fooled around with anyone else

on Audry not to say I would have fucked a thousand times under the right circumstances but the
circumstances were never right before I couldn't
get my mind off him all day I couldn't eat or
concentrate on my work the guys teased what
was wrong today when I got out of work I went
home and called Audry she was coming home in
a couple of days and then I went down to The
Other Side to see if he was there but didn't recognize anyone so I went down the Zone and
started drinking bourbon and cokes and watching some strip shows but my mind was on him
when the girls came around looking for some
company I gave them all the cold shoulder later I
went back down The Other Side and he still was-
n't there but a friend of his this black kid who
was really beautiful in drag and wore a blond
wig said Craig was supposed to meet him that
afternoon but never showed and he was beginning to worry something was wrong so we went
out driving around looking for Craig and that's
when I found out he was on drugs again and his
mother wasn't dead his parents were divorced
and she lived in California and I was asking
myself what the fuck I was doing in the middle
of all of this when Craig's friend pointed him

out getting out of a car he was in full dress the
same outfit he wore the night before and the car
drove away and we pulled over to the curb when
he recognized us he got in the back seat and we
drove to The Other Side he seemed drunk again
but by then I knew it must be drugs I never knew
anybody on the hard drugs before he was slow in
his talking but acting more girlish than ever at
the bar we had a couple of drinks and I asked
him did he have a place to stay he said no I asked
him where would he go he said he'd find a bed
someplace so I got another room for the night
and I didn't mean to because I went looking for
him in the first place to tell him that what happened was fine but it couldn't happen again and
my family came first I couldn't put anything at
risk and now we were back in a room together
all over each other and this time we spent the
night he did things even the chicks in Korea
never did there wasn't one part of my body he
didn't know how to touch right I was crazy for it
and I fucked him so hard the flesh on my cock
got raw and when Audry got back it still had
some marks but we didn't have sex for a couple
of days after so it worked out ok when I was a
kid one Sunday at mass the priest made a ser-

mon about this guy who lived all alone who never went to church he had no friends or family when he died and they went into his room in the cheap rooming house all they found besides his few clothes and things were boxes full of dirty magazines of the most evil kind and it got me real hard listening to him talk and how he said of the most evil kind and I remember how wrong it must be to get a boner in church I couldn't stop thinking about what must be in all those dirty magazines in Frank's magazines there was mostly naked girls and sometimes naked girls doing things with guys once I had to stay home from school with the flu and Ma was working at the time at the Converse Factory and I was home alone and I beat off so many times with Frank's magazines my dick got raw then too and I couldn't touch it for over a week it scabbed up that was the same priest who said mass at Ma's funeral only then he looked so old I thought he might die before the mass was done I thought that they let priests retire but who knows there was hardly anyone at Ma's funeral the church felt empty and she was all shriveled up and tinier than ever in the casket it was like yesterday she was up and around shouting at us in Italian to clean up for dinner or clean up our mess or clean up for bed or clean up so we could go out and find Pa there's no doubt that Pa was a rat but he was still my father no matter how bad he was and you have to show a little respect no matter what Peter used to get all worked up when Pa even got mentioned but Peter had it worse than anybody except Ma of course Pa never hit me I remember him hitting Frank sometimes and when Frank got older he stopped hitting him but it was Peter Pa hated mostly if he didn't hit Ma he hit Peter after Peter's little girl was born he started drinking a little more and roughed up Teresa who called the police one time and they took Peter down the station Peter called me and I had to go down to the station with Teresa and the police wanted her to sign this thing where she could press charges but she said she didn't want to press charges she just wanted Peter to stop hitting her then he would be good for a while then out of the blue I'd get a call from Teresa Peter was drinking and I'd have to go over and smooth things out I don't know what Peter wanted he had a wife and child and had a pension at the factory and made decent money but when he had a few drinks he started feeling sorry

for himself saying things like he was a loser and
a freak usually I got him calmed down and into
bed he slept it off when Audry got back from
North Carolina I couldn't think of anything but
Craig but I told him I couldn't see him any more
I cared for him and wanted to help him get back
on his feet but my family came first and what
happened couldn't happen again I thought it for
the best that we stay out of touch but if he needed to call me he should only call me at the store
and never at home my feelings went back and
forth between this huge guilt that somehow I'd
gone against my vows to Audry and after years
of staying true to her I strayed and worse I
strayed with a boy not much older than my son
of course Craig was street-wise and years
beyond little Tony that way but it was still wrong
what I did even though in my heart I believed
that sex is sex and two people can love each
other and have sex with other people and shit
you could even love more than one person I
mean I loved Audry when she got back from
North Carolina but I was obsessed with this kid
I stopped eating and shitting Audry wasn't ready
to just jump into bed after we had been apart
and that was ok with me cause I wasn't feeling

like it anyway I wasn't jerking off and even when I thought of Craig I thought of holding him and taking care of him not having sex with him I couldn't think straight it worked to my advantage because Audry thought I was all messed up cause of us almost breaking up and the problems we were having I truly wanted to get back on track with the marriage at first I had a hard time looking the boys in the eye because I felt such guilt and I took everyone out for supper and we went to the Burlington Mall and the boys and Audry shopped all day and Audry and I had late night heart to heart talks about how she was feeling and that she loved me but I was very hard to love and over the years I'd grown distant and all I cared about was work and being the number one salesman and with all the work on the house and the time I spent doing things for my brothers and sisters and Ma it didn't leave that much time for us or time for me with the boys I half listened quietly and was I not thinking about Craig I would have really got pissed after all everything I did I did for Audry and the boys I wanted to give them what I never had I never wanted them to want for anything and they never did there was always plenty of food in the house and Audry

never had to go chasing me out of some bar I
was always home when I wasn't at work and it
wasn't easy working as hard at the store as I did
and keeping up with all the work the house
needed over the years but I shook my head like I
agreed with Audry and in a way I guess she was
right about some things but I couldn't get my
mind off him that night Audry and me went to
bed and we made real hard love straight ahead
just me on top but I was ramming her hard and
she liked it in between telling me to go easy and
when she fell asleep I laid there in bed with my
eyes wide open fighting the urge to go out and
look for him instead I just laid there and about
three in the morning I knew I wasn't going to get
to sleep I tapped Audry and told her that I
was going out for a drive she said I love you
and be careful as I left and I drove up to New
Hampshire but instead of turning around I kept
driving and the time it was getting light I could
see the mountains off in the distance but I could-
n't remember a thing since I'd passed my usual
exit then turned around at the next one and
speeded home Audry and the boys were having
breakfast and I told them about my drive and
how beautiful the mountains were and how next

summer we would all take a vacation up there I never saw the White Mountains before and they were only two hours away I drove into work wondering how I would get through the day so tired but I had one of my best days of the season by now Mr Sanford was gone and replaced by Ms Hollingsworth as personnel manager and in our annual meeting she said that she thought I would make a good division manager had I ever given it any thought in fact I had but only years ago now I would have to take a cut in pay to be a division manager it was said I made more money than anybody in the store except for the store manager she said she would think it might be nice after all these years to get out of the pressure of working straight commission but I'd rather work on straight commission it was kind of like working for yourself a division manager got a salary and had to work extra hours and all that sure it looked good you were a division manager and you got to carry around a clipboard but who needed it I didn't hear from Craig and me and Audry were doing ok I had to either block Craig out of my mind or I did nothing but think of him some days I thought that I was in love with him other days I just felt so guilty for

what I did that was the year we took the vacation
to Disney in Florida and Gina and Maria came
too we had a great time it was the best time we
all had together ever we stayed at this big hotel
and it was the first real vacation I took in my life
since being out of the Marines I mean when I got
out of the Marines I didn't work for a while but
it wasn't really a vacation I was looking for work
and all the years since working at Pratt's every
time I had time off I worked on the house and
having the time off down in Florida got me
thinking about my own business again I wasn't
getting any younger and I had some good money
built up in profit sharing and a big savings
account over the years the property in Somerville
started going up and I had the house paid off so
we were sitting pretty good I didn't want to
spend the next twenty years at Pratt's there had
to be more so when we got back I started looking around again but there was mostly just pizza
shops and breakfast joints and that didn't seem
right for me then one day I got a call from Craig
again it was strange because it was just long
enough since I heard from him before that I was
starting to feel like maybe it never even happened and since Florida I was eating again and

shitting again regular and even getting five or six hours of sleep a night Audry and me were getting it on once in a while cause for the longest time the first thing when I opened my eyes in the morning would be to get this sinking feeling in my stomach thinking of him and then when he called I had that feeling all over again I told him it wouldn't be good to see him and that it was best we let everything go he said don't you think about what we had and I told him I did I thought it was beautiful but it was what it was and he said he had nowhere else to turn but if that's what I really meant that was ok I gave in and told him I would meet him after work I called Audry and told her I was going out for drinks with the guys I could tell by the tone of her voice that she suspected something this was the first time since she got back from North Carolina I was going out she asked me who was going and I told her and she asked me where we were going I told her I wasn't sure but I'd be home early I met Craig down The Other Side and he looked real bad he wasn't in drag but just jeans and a t-shirt worn-out sneakers and no socks he was dirty and it was the first time I ever noticed he had a beard and there was stubble he looked older and

real high said he was on the street again and
admitted he was strung out but he said he was
going into the clinic and going to clean his act up
this time but he needed some money if I could
lend him some as he promised he'd pay it back
cause soon as he was clean he was going to get a
job and go to college part-time at night but I
didn't want to give him anything if he was going
to spend it on drugs I made him swear to me that
he wouldn't use the money for dope and he
swore he said there was a friend he could live
with if he could come up with some rent money
it would be easier after he got out of the clinic to
get back on his feet if he had a place to go to but
I only had about fifty bucks on me and the banks
were closed until the next day so on the way to
work the next morning I took out five hundred
bucks and on my lunch break went to meet him
in Harvard Square it was easy for me to get at
the money without Audry knowing cause I han-
dled all the money Audry never knew how much
was in the savings or the checking account I kept
the bank book and paid all the bills Audry hated
doing that stuff and could never balance the
books otherwise there was no way I could give
the money to Craig but I did and like the night

before he tried to kiss me but I held him off even though I was tempted and wanted him I told him to call if he needed anything cause I believed in him he was a smart kid and could do anything in the world he wanted he said I was the only one in his shitty life who really cared for him and he would always remember me I didn't hear from him after that for a while but I started thinking about him again it even got to my work cause that month for the first time in ten years as a big-ticket salesman and being number one I was third and Mike Cordano who was second behind me all those years got first I knew why I slipped I lost my concentration and started taking long coffee breaks and daydreaming the guys at work called it middle-age crisis I didn't really understand what all that shit meant except that I was bald and a lot heavier I still felt like I was twenty-one but it didn't even bother me that I was third and the next month I was second and for the first time in six years I didn't win the annual Easy Payment Plan promotion award and one day the division manager took me aside and asked me was everything all right I told him yes he said if I needed to talk to anyone I could talk to him we went back a lot of years we did I

always respected Mr Zizzo most of the guys
hated him he seemed like a hard-ass but that was
just his job he was the kind of guy that on his
days off went to lectures on history and stuff
and liked to read but at work he was always on
our backs if we were selling too much advertised
product and not enough service policies and saying old Mrs Howe from the stationery department could outsell us he liked to keep us at each
other so he would do a lot baiting one guy
against the other only Faith wasn't a guy and
over the years everybody respected her cause she
pretty much did as well as any of the guys and
didn't let anything get to her she took long coffee breaks and lunches but when she latched on
to a customer she didn't let go until she sold top-
of-the-line I think the ladies trusted buying from
her cause they figured she knew more about
things like washers and dryers and stoves being a
chick at that time Frank was living with a new
girlfriend who had a daughter who was seventeen built like a dream he told me he was doing
her too and the mother knew and it was ok with
the mother I thought that was really fucked up
and I told him so I never told Frank about Craig
I never told anyone about Craig and that made it

hard cause there was no one I could talk to about it to try and figure things out I didn't know what I really wanted I mean how could I be realistic and think there was anything in the future for us it was crazy and I was a sick fuck when I took a look around me I felt even worse with my brother Frank doing his girlfriend's daughter and Peter still drinking beating up on Teresa and even my little Tony suffered cause kids have a way of picking up on things even if you don't think they do but he was getting bigger and bigger and the school doctor sent home a note we should help him eat better and get him on a diet we tried Audry cooked special things for him and he didn't seem to eat much at home but Audry would find empty bags of candy chips and cupcakes hidden in his room he wasn't doing good at school they said it wasn't that he was stupid but he didn't concentrate too good I tried talking to him and for a while we went on a diet together we both lost weight but I had this kind of double life part of me was where I should be with my home and family and part of me wanted to be somewhere else a day didn't go by without thinking about Craig and where he was and why didn't he call to let me know how things were working out because he promised he would sometimes fighting off the temptation to go out and look for him between me and Audry it seemed like the same old bickering like for almost twenty years we were together we got to really hate each other as much as we loved each other and I loved her a lot then I started looking around for some kind of business of my own again I went to seminars and went to the library and the lady helped me get books out on small businesses I was ready to make the move as soon as the right thing came along there were so many different kinds of things I almost bought a van so I could start a business picking people up at the grocery market and taking them home then there were the sales things cause being good at sales a lot of the franchises said I would do real good with products you could sell from your house then I thought maybe I could get a real-estate license and start my own agency but nothing seemed right one Sunday I went to this convention in Boston with all these different franchise people and there was this soft ice cream franchise you could open six months a year and make enough to close the other half of the year so I almost bought a place that was already in operation it was in Lawrence and one Sunday afternoon after dinner I took the whole family up there and everybody seemed excited except Audry who thought Lawrence was far away to have a business we might have to sell the house and move closer Audry had wanted for a long time to move out into the suburbs but I had lived all my life in Somerville and after all the years of working on the house and finally having it in shape it was all paid for I got to feeling that I wouldn't leave the house ever but Audry would leave in a second she wanted more than anything a single family somewhere and Gina could take care of herself she was an office manager and making good money there was only Frank and after all the years of beating me for the rent I should let him fend for himself but there was something about the house that held me there and I could always see Ma sitting at the window and remember carrying little Tony up the stairs from the hospital after he was born that it was the only real home I ever had so it was hard to think of giving it up besides the suburbs were so quiet and nothing ever seemed to be going on there were so many kinds of different people in Somerville and Broadway was a main street so there was a lot of cars and trucks and people on foot all hours of the day and night you could hear people and engines and horns and sirens you get used to knowing something is going on out there that's why I loved New York City so much all that kind of energy I still can't believe old Ma packed us kids up got us there and we ended up safe so many things could have gone wrong the day Ma sent Gina out for some dry beans at the market which was just next door to the downstairs baker and Gina went the wrong way and didn't come back we couldn't find her and for a couple of hours it was the worst feeling I remember really understanding how huge that city is how it could just eat you up and finally someone found Gina crying on a street corner ten blocks away and they called the cops we had already talked with the neighborhood cop and they brought Gina back in a squad car Ma was hysteric screaming and cursing praising God and all the saints she lit candles and said novenas every day for months after that when I was young I loved church and for a while I wanted to be a priest Ma said she always thought I would be a good priest I loved the candles and the smell of the incense I became an altar boy and learned some of the Latin I remember standing up next to the altar on Sunday mornings with all the lit candles and the music on the organ blaring loud and Ma sitting in the front row tears in her eyes seeing me and I loved when I was the one who got to ring the bells there was a married couple who used to sit in the front row every eight-thirty mass and she was pretty and I used to think about her a lot when I jerked off so I got to look forward to eight-thirty mass and seeing her there every Sunday morning then when Father Leonard started hearing all the altar boys' confession he started asking stuff about my thoughts and did I touch myself what did I think about when I touched myself I never told him about the lady in the front row at the eight-thirty mass but I did say that I lied so I hoped that would cover it later Skipper Capraro told me that Father Leonard gave him a blow job in the confessional and told him if he ever told anybody he would go to hell for sure I figured Father Leonard was doing himself in the confessional when he asked people all those questions but hey everybody jerks off and priests know it and the nuns know it too but they say a lot of nuns get it on with each other you would think they might get it on with the priests but the priests they say get it on with each other or have a mistress but there was something about Sunday mornings at church and the rituals you need those kinds of things to help bring life into some kind of balance even though I mostly stopped going to church especially after Ma died but I always respected the church and priests and nuns too there's something special about those kinds of people who have a calling but how the fuck are you supposed to go without sex no one can you can put a guy in the seminary but you can't stop him from jerking off I always tried to give the boys as much privacy as possible when I was a kid I had none and I was always trying to figure out how to be alone so that I could jerk off without someone around the house I told Audry to always make sure she gave the boys as much privacy as possible so that they didn't have to worry about that stuff one time Audry found some magazines in little Tony's room when she was looking for food I told her leave them it was normal for little Tony to be doing that kind of thing she wanted to take the magazines and throw them away but I wouldn't let her besides if we threw them away little Tony would know that we knew and were going through his things it would be embarrassing for him little Tony already had a kind of complex about that stuff being over-weight he didn't have a girlfriend and didn't go to his high-school dances or proms I figured he could at least find one of the fat girls at school he didn't take to other things at school like sports or clubs Johnny was interested in science and math and didn't have no trouble with girls being interested in him but he wasn't all that interested in them it was like he'd rather have his nose in a book I don't know where all that came from I don't know of anyone in the family who was ever book smart Johnny was a first I think if we had sent the boys to regular high school little Tony would have done even worse than he did and might have got into more trouble it wasn't serious stuff but little Tony seemed to be some-times in the wrong place at the wrong time like one day when he was younger we got a call from one of the sisters she said little Tony started a fire in a waste-paper basket I had to go up the school and talk to the mother superior little Tony said it wasn't him that lit the fire it was someone else but he didn't want to say who but the mother superior said that Sister Gloria who-

TONY LUONGO

ever knew for sure it was little Tony I had to
punish him it was hard to punish little Tony
cause if you made him stay in it was ok with him
he hardly ever went out anyway mostly he
watched television and ate snacks so we took
television away from him for a month but it only
lasted a week the poor kid maybe he didn't light
the fire when they accused him of carving the
words cunt and prick into the wooden desktop
he said it wasn't him it was there one day after
public school kids took catechism class in the
room it's hard not to believe your kid when they
look you right in the eye and say they didn't do
something I knew he was having a hard time it's
tough for kids trying to figure things out and he
seen some fucked-up things at home with Frank
living there all the years and even me when I lost
my temper but no matter what I always told the
boys I love you no matter how messed up things
must seem to them at certain times with Audry
and me having problems they should always
remember that I loved them and I would do anything for them when I finally got a call from
Craig it was almost as if what happened with me
and him was some kind of dream and I couldn't
remember was it last night or last year or five

years I thought of him less and less but I still found myself when my guard was down remembering how I felt during that sex we had and wondering was he ok imagining where he might be and did he ever think of me he said he was doing good and thought of me a lot but didn't call cause he knew I wanted to stay away but he wanted to let me know he was doing ok and soon would be taking the test to get his high-school diploma he was working at a hardware store downtown but he just lost his job cause business was slow so instead of laying him off so he could at least collect they fired him for some stupid reason now he was out of work again but looking and he wondered if I might like to meet him for coffee and as easy as if someone from the store just asked did I want to go for coffee I said yes and the next day I had to work an evening shift so I left a little early and met him he didn't look too good but he said he was staying off drugs since he got out of the clinic he only slipped once or twice and a few times he was going to go get some he thought of me and what I did for him and it helped him stay strong so I gave him a couple of hundred dollars and drove him to his father's house in Dorchester cause he

moved back in with his family he leaned over
and kissed me and the little fuck took my breath
away right there I had all I could do to hold
myself back those old feelings about him came
back to me I told him it couldn't happen again
but for days after that all I could think of was
him and it was during the time when I started
looking for a business again so the next time he
called me I met him the next day which was my
day off and I told Audry I was driving down to
Fall River to look at a pizza place and we spent
the day in a motel by then I knew I was helpless
when it came to Craig I would do anything for
the next couple of months it went like that once
or twice a week I would tell Audry I was going to
look at a business someplace and I would meet
Craig sometimes we would just get a room and
sometimes we would go out to The Other Side
for drinks sometimes when I picked him up he
was dressed and other times he wasn't it's
strange how after a while he seemed to be Craig
to me whether he was dressed like a chick or a
guy funny thing when he was dressed like a chick
it brought out his manly side you noticed more
his boy's beard or muscled hands and when he
was just a guy he looked more like a chick his

skin was soft and his hands looked delicate and
every time we met I gave him money fifty here a
hundred there he didn't seem to be using drugs
and passed his test so he got his high-school
diploma and as soon as he got a job he was
going to go to college part-time and after all the
years of Audry knowing my every move I had the
perfect alibi with the business thing and I was
amazed at how easy it was to do it and to have
this other life Audry's sisters and mother kept
sending her real estate flyers and business listings
and telling her how much better we could do
with our money down there so she was always
kind of relieved when I got home from one of
my visits to a business for sale and said it was
lousy for one reason or another she was secretly
hoping I would get discouraged and consider
moving down to North Carolina the only cousin
I kept in touch with lived up in Tewksbury Leo
grew up in Somerville but he bought three acres
of land and was growing his own food and had
chickens and went out every morning to gather
eggs and milk his goats they had no television
and Leo was real strict with his kids like after
school they always had plenty of chores to do
they weren't allowed to hang out with other kids

he said it was a crazy world and he was going to keep his kids away from all that evil stuff he was a religious guy too always telling me Tony you have to read the Bible it's all there and Jesus can save me too and I should move out there and get out of the rat race I lived in there was no meaning to it but the last place I could live in is the country milking goats and cutting firewood no fucking way besides I told him he needed to give his kids some freedom if he didn't he would be sorry cause you can't build a wall around yourself it'll crack no doubt about it kids need to be kids that was part of Craig's problem he never had a chance to be a kid and if there's one thing I gave my boys it was space and time to be kids and not put a lot of pressure on them no one's perfect as a parent but one rule of thumb for me was to think about how I felt when I was a kid when you put yourself in a kid's place sometimes it helps and things just went on like that with me and Craig I figured out he was still using drugs but I still gave him money I always made him promise he wouldn't buy drugs but I knew he would so when we were together I tried to get him to eat we would go to Chinatown and I'd order a lot of food he just sat and picked at a

chicken wing for an hour I would force him to
eat some rice and vegetables he was so skinny his
bones were showing through his flesh I had the
waiter wrap the leftovers and wherever I dropped
him off he walked away holding a brown bag full
of food I wondered did he just throw it in a trash
can after I drove away then I didn't hear from
him for a few weeks and I got real worried it was
strange because I didn't just care about helping
him any more now I wanted to be with him it
wasn't just the sex sometimes we didn't even
have sex though even when he was real high he
tried to give me a blow job but I wouldn't let him
it got kind of sad and the more I wanted to be
with him the worse I felt about myself that I was
able to just be another person when I walked
into my home and saw Audry and the boys they
would ask what was it like and I would make up
some laundry or pizza shop and how if it only
had better parking I might have been interested
and things were pretty good between me and
Audry at that time that's what was really strange
cause we were getting along talking better
though we long since stopped fucking regular
except on our anniversary or birthday though
sometimes she jerked me off but she never want-

ed me just to do her with my hand or mouth she just did the hand job thing out of some sense of duty but it was good and I must say she had a strong wrist and got the job done at work I was just not into it any more when you lose your concentration you just can't do your best it was a year since I'd been number one Faith had become top salesman in major appliances and all the guys walked around the store with their tails between their legs when the monthly figures were posted I thought it was great more power to her then they started talking about putting more chicks in major appliances since Faith did so well and all the guys started getting uptight and about that time the economy was slowing the stocks were down and my profit sharing was getting less and less I was thinking that if I didn't do something soon I would never have enough to buy a business there was this building right across the street from my house for sale it used to be a hair dressing shop for years it was cheap and the right size for an ice cream stand up and down Broadway there was not one ice cream stand in the summer people either had to wait for when the ice cream man came around or drive someplace everybody said I was crazy that

I'd lose my shirt but I figured it out how much it would cost to fix the place up then how much I might bring in a day for the six months we were open and I wouldn't have to pay too much for help cause I could work it myself and the boys could help and Audry too the house was paid for so we didn't have a lot of expenses no one knew how much I had in the savings account but it was a lot more than Audry ever figured and I could get the place up and running with only investing my profit sharing from twenty years at the store Frank wanted in right away and asked to be a partner but there was no way I would do it because Frank had no money I wouldn't be partners with him anyway then I figured out that he was only looking to have a place he could run a gambling business I was used to Frank it could have been any of my brothers and sisters who had something wrong with them and needed to be taken care of the girls had done great Josie was the first one in the family to graduate college had a good husband and good kid and another on the way and Gina all the years stayed on the second floor paying her utilities but I never took any rent from her even after Ma died she did good and her daughter Maria was in this

national honor society at school and was going
to be a teacher we didn't hear much from Peter
unless he was causing trouble at home and
Teresa would call they mostly kept to themselves
his daughter and Teresa never left each other's
sides except when Anna was in school they mostly stayed in the house and had no friends and
sometimes Peter showed up at our house drunk
pulling his routine about poor me life sucks I got
tired of it and angry with him but the poor fuck
never had a chance in the first place so what
could I do but be a brother Ma made me
promise before she died that I would take care of
everybody and I could still see her in the window
it's funny cause Ma always seemed old to me
when I think about that time she lived with us on
Broadway she was blind for at least ten years she
spent her days at the window even though she
couldn't see so if you walked by the house there
was Ma looking out the second-floor window
but she couldn't see you I wish she could have
lived long enough for little Tony's graduation
from high school Audry and me were worried
about little Tony he didn't have good enough
grades to get into college he didn't want to go
anyway and once when he was a senior and I

found out he was playing pool after I told him I wanted him to stay out of the pool halls I went down the pool hall and I took the stick out of his hand and broke it on the table and dragged him out by his ear then I found out Audry knew he was playing pool and I went even crazier she said she didn't tell me cause she knew if she did I would do exactly what I did which was go crazy and act like an idiot and that as long as she knew he was there and he wasn't playing for money she was glad that he told her the truth about where he was spending his time and I was the one who always said that you got to give the kids space and let them enjoy being young so I got little Tony a job at the store on the loading dock when he graduated high school he was doing ok out there and learning a little about the value of a dollar I told him as long as he lived at home he wouldn't have to pay any board or nothing but he did have to save part of his money I think Audry was glad when I got little Tony into the store she figured that it was a good way to make sure that I wasn't doing anything I shouldn't be doing she was always suspicious about the store and all the chicks thinking that I was trying to do one of them and when I was having this thing with Craig she never even got suspicious so it kind of started to go on and on but after about six months he got worse and seemed to be more drugged out every time I saw him he was always asking for money and I was always giving it to him then once he showed up at the store and it really shook me up I was on the point and there he was coming down the escalator looking at me in that girlish way he did fortunately it was a morning so there were only two of us on and Faith was on her coffee break so I headed him off and told him he couldn't come here he said he knew but I was his last resort and I told him to go out in the parking lot I would meet him there in a few minutes Faith came back I told her I was taking a coffee break and went out to the lot he said he needed a car could he borrow mine it would only be for a couple of hours I told him when he brought it back to leave it unlocked with the keys in the glove box and not come back into the store at lunch I went out he still hadn't brought the car back and afternoon coffee break it was the same I was getting real nervous cause if he didn't have the car back when I got out of work I'd have to make up something to tell Audry about what happened to the car

when I got out of work he was just pulling up
and he had this look on his face like something
was wrong then I looked at the side of the car
where it was sideswiped he said he had the car
parked in a lot and when he got back he found it
that way he was sorry and would pay for the
repair because the reason he needed the car in
the first place was that he spent the day on job
interviews he thought he had a job and the first
thing he was going to do was pay me back I
could tell he was high and drove him into town
he wanted me to leave him off at The Other Side
so I did but I made my mind up on the way there
that it had to stop and I told him so whatever it
was that was going on between us had to stop it
wasn't that I cared about the money or anything
it was him I cared about I told him so and I was-
n't doing anything good for him by giving him
money cause there's only one thing he did with
the money it wasn't a case any more that I could
help him but I couldn't help him until he was
ready to help himself it wasn't like there was
anything in the future for us it was all crazy he
still had his future ahead of him he shouldn't
waste it you're so sweet and nobody ever cared
for me like you do he said with his sad blue eyes

looking at me but I wouldn't kiss him I told him
no matter what he shouldn't call me and if some
day he got straight and his life was squared away
I would like to hear about how he ended up but
if he continued on the road he was on he was
only going to end up dead or in jail and he
would never find anyone who really cared about
him and could give him the kind of love a person
needs unless he was into a better lifestyle and off
drugs he said you're so sweet and touched my
nose with his finger and off he went into the bar
and that's the last I saw of him for about six
months I stopped going out to look at businesses
and was getting real crabby around the house
Audry and me were fighting a lot then once in a
while in the middle of a fight we'd end up in bed
having some wild fucking how do you figure and
I got to hand it to Audry she kept her shape over
the years she didn't gain more than five pounds
in all the years together and still looked as good
in a pair of jeans as she did when I first laid my
eyes on her ass in the marking room all those
years before sometimes I thought of Craig and
wondered where he was there were days when I
had all I could do to hold myself back from
going downtown to find him but then it would

go away I'd be ok for a while then Audry went
down to North Carolina for a week and the boys
wanted to go too cause her mother wasn't doing
too good she had lung cancer and only had
about a year to go Audry said Tony under the
circumstances I think you should think about
going down with us but in twenty years all that
mother and the sisters ever did was make my life
miserable plotting at every chance they could to
figure out ways to get Audry to leave me and
move back to North Carolina but at this point in
time I knew Audry would never leave unless
something really bad happened and when her
mother died she wouldn't want to go back to
North Carolina as far as I was concerned the
bitch couldn't die soon enough but I didn't tell
Audry that I just said there was no way I was
going down there her mother never showed me
one bit of respect or acknowledged even that I
had done a lot and given Audry a good home
and family Audry never had to want for nothing
but that old crust thought that her daughters
should be all living in mansions or something
like on *Dallas* that's why she never kept a husband she either buried them or left them cause
they couldn't give her the kind of lifestyle she

expected if I wanted to work she said I would have stayed single the fucking bitch grew up in a trailer park and she thought she should be sleeping in satin sheets so even though Audry said it might be the last chance to see her mother alive in some ways out of respect I knew she was right but there was no way I was going and the first couple of nights she was away I thought about trying to find Craig and over the past few months Angela Rizzio who worked part-time in jewelry was nosing around and I knew that she and Phil Burns from automotive were having a thing for a while Angela and her friend Tricia both worked at the store part-time and since they'd been there which was a year or so they had a bit of a reputation Tricia was already fooling around with Mr Sarcia the controller he was married with kids she was divorced and had a teenage daughter who was a looker too and one day Jimmy Wilson on maintenance walked into a supply closet and Tricia was on her knees giving Mr Sarcia a blow job Angela was married and her husband had a television repair business in Arlington she had two beautiful kids and a nice house everything a person wants but she still had that itch and she wasn't like Tricia cause

Tricia only fooled around with guys in the store who had some pull and she was already in line for a big-ticket job even though she had only been working part-time for a year but Angela she fooled around cause she liked it she already had the things she wanted she just wanted a good time and one night after work when Audry was away a few of the guys and Angela and Tricia were going out for drinks so I went along over the years I drank less and less so I got drunk pretty easy and once I felt it there was no stopping me so I was feeling good and talking a lot about sex it was the seventies and during the seventies it seems a lot of people were talking about sex we all got drunk and I was picking up on Angela's vibes she was cute a few years younger than me short dirty blond hair and one of those tight small bodies she still looked great even though she had a couple of kids and was about thirty-five and she always dressed real nice and wore make-up and had this beauty mark on the lower left side of her cheek that drove me crazy a few times at the store when I did some flirting with her she seemed to respond and flirt a little back I never thought nothing of it til that night sitting there I realized I wanted her so bad and as it got later we ended up sitting next to each other at the table getting out of the general conversation she said it was rare to see me out with people from the store I told her my wife was away one thing led to another and we were in my car in the parking lot making out she jerked me off and blew me I fingered her and she fingered herself and we both came it was incredible and then she asked me did I want to smoke I told her I didn't she said no pot I was already drunk so I took a few puffs and man I was really high and we started making out and getting into it again the pot made me feel real weird and I thought I was getting sick then there was a bang on the window and I almost jumped through the roof of the car it was a cop who said that we had to move on and so we kissed goodnight she went off in her car to her house and family in Arlington and I went home to the empty apartment in Somerville I wasn't there five minutes when Audry called and I was pretty high from the pot and bourbon and cokes so I had a hard time concentrating on what I said she asked me where I had been all night I told her I was out with some people from work and she asked who and I made the mistake of mentioning Angela and Tricia Audry got really uptight and said that her mother was dying and I was out having a party with the store sluts I told her I wasn't going to listen to that shit hung up and left the phone off the hook then I passed out that was the only time Angela and me ever did anything besides flirt it's not that I wouldn't if I had the chance I thought she was real hot and for the first couple of weeks after that night I was hornier than I'd been in a long time then I found out she was fooling around with one of the younger part-timers I thought to myself why would she want me shit I was overweight and bald when she still had her looks I was lucky and I thought of that night a lot when I jerked off there was something about her not just her looks but about how she was with sex like she could just hop in my car and get it on with me and do herself like that without no hang-ups it's kind of the way I felt but I didn't fool around for so many years by the time I did I couldn't help but feel a little guilty she could just go home to her family and still be a good mother and wife why not it was so different from Audry who was real suspicious when she got back from North Carolina that's one of the reasons why even if I could have got something going with Angela at the time I wouldn't have been able I had to stay close to home Audry was watching me like a hawk every time Audry got back from North Carolina she looked real good like either her hair was different or she got a little sun but she always knew how to fill a pair of jeans and me being so horny at the time we started getting it on a little but as usual most of the time Audry was just doing it to satisfy me and I could tell if she was blowing me or jerking me off or something she was doing it out of duty if I made a move to go down on her she would say no why don't you just come inside I don't think she came too often mostly she would work on getting me off so she could get it over with then sometimes I wondered to myself does Audry not like sex or does she not like sex with me I asked her is it me and she said no but she had to be having some sex I asked her did she do herself sometimes she said you know I don't like to talk about those things and so it went on for a while I started to dread going to work and that was such a change from years before when I used to look forward to it and charge into the major appliances at the beginning of my day like I was going to conquer

the world now I went through the motions since
I had it down so good I still made pretty good
money but I took coffee breaks and long lunches
things I never used to do I flirted a lot those were
wild times with sex and drugs some of the young
chicks they hired were really crazy flirted a lot
but they were mostly interested in the younger
guys I would have left the store but the economy
was so bad and the stocks were low my profit
sharing was only about half of what it was two
years before then when Audry's mother died I
wasn't going to go to North Carolina with her
we had a big fight screaming at each other actually I did most of the screaming Audry cried and
said I was never there for her when she needed
me right after she left I got this real strange feeling like I fucked up bad so without even getting
any clothes or anything I got a cab and went to
the airport and ran around from different desks
trying to find out Audry's flight and made it on
the plane at the very last minute she didn't talk
to me all the way down the boys were sad cause
she was the only grandparent they had left she
was always good to them and they loved her but
I only stayed for two days that was long enough
with all the cold shoulders I was getting from

her bitch sisters they're all crying and acting sad and I know them cunts they couldn't wait to get their hands on the old lady's money cause each time she buried or divorced a husband she had more of it and I know that at least one of Audry's sisters couldn't stand the mother Audry told me everybody knew but she played the good daughter through the whole thing of the mother being sick with cancer and all cause she knew some of that money was going to her and the mother left all of it to the girls including the big house she owned which the sisters had on the market before the poor old bitch was cold in the grave Audry got one fourth of it and I told her she could do whatever she wanted with it we didn't need it I didn't want her family's money anyway but I went right back home and Audry stayed for a while to help settle things and Johnny stayed there with Audry cause he was on summer vacation and little Tony came back with me cause he quit his job at Pratt's and was work-ing in a sporting goods warehouse outside of Union Square and being around Audry's family after her mother died got me thinking about Ma and her funeral since she was gone I thought less and less of my past cause when Ma was around every day there she was to remind me and say things like remember when we were in New York and ate the hard bread with the watery hot cocoa and remember when you got back from Korea and we all were at the airport waiting for you to get off the plane that afternoon seeing them all lined up there even Frank Ma Peter Gina Josie but with Ma gone I remembered things from when I was younger when I least expected like out of nowhere I would think of my father crawling up the stairs calling for Ma to put on the water and no matter what she was doing or what time of day Ma would drop what she was doing put the water on and make Pa a dish of macaroni even when he ate he kept drinking he would cause a scene over something or other I never knew the Pa in the picture Ma kept on her mantle she said I looked like him and I guess I did he was kind of short and stocky too with the pointed nose and no chin and even at twenty he was half bald he looked sober in that picture and had a smile I never saw him with who would have thought that man in the photo was capable of some of the shit that Pa pulled over the years Ma used to say in the end it was good he died it was a chance for Ma to have a

real life and have some peace cause even after she
got back from New York and her sister helped
her get the paper that said Pa could never go
near Ma again Ma was always afraid cause Pa
always said he'd kill her if she ever left him and
she used to say that as long as he was alive she
had to look over her shoulder and she believed
that's why she went blind having to strain to
keep an eye out for Pa but Ma Pa's been dead for
years I had to tell her maybe no she said maybe
no it was sad to think how much she had to go
through trying to keep the family together without a real husband around and how no matter
how little there was to eat she made it go around
so we didn't go hungry she always had a story
about when she was a girl in Italy and her first
boyfriend who she kissed in the olive grove but
her family made her marry my father who she
wouldn't have married if she had to choose there
were a few times at Christmas there was just no
money Ma was able to come up with enough to
put a good meal together I still remember homemade macaroni and meatballs and it was the
first time we ate meat in a month and she knew
we were sad cause we didn't get toys and she
made us bundle up and we went on the bus and

subway to some place downtown where people didn't have homes it was a shelter she said it was bad for us but not as bad as it was for others that always stuck with me and that's why from the time I got back from the Marines every year on Christmas I volunteered my mornings at a shelter helping prepare the Christmas meal actually I was never much of a cook I used to peel potatoes and wash the pots and pans out and one time I brought Audry and the boys there and made them eat Christmas dinner but they said it wasn't fair that they should have to eat their Christmas dinner there just cause I wanted to and Audry said she wouldn't do it again so after that I went alone for the early part of the day before we had Christmas dinner at home but I forgot it was my mother sent me to that place every year being a kid and realizing people had it even worse than us I never forgot it Audry called and said she was going to take another week and maybe even longer cause things were pretty screwed up with her mother's estate and Johnny was having a good time with some of his cousins her sisters all had kids with different guys who could keep track of them and except that when Audry was away I had to do my own clothes and shoes and cooking so I just ate out or got subs I kind of liked being on my own and little Tony came and went on his own and worked hard at his job he still liked to play pool but I figured at least I knew where he was at night for a while he liked this girl from work and went on a diet and lost about thirty pounds then something happened she started dating some other dude he put the weight right back on then one of those nights before Audry got back from North Carolina I was working the late shift at the store and after we closed at nine-thirty out of nowhere I felt this urge to go see Craig I didn't talk to him or see him for a long time and really didn't think of him much that day but between walking out of the store and getting into my car in the parking lot I made up my mind I was going to look for him so I drove down the South End and went to The Other Side but he wasn't around I had a drink with one of his friends who said that Craig wasn't doing good but he hadn't seen him for a few days I had another bourbon and coke and started to feel good and left The Other Side and down to the Zone to one of the strip clubs and when I got there a beautiful young chick was wiggling her ass at guys sitting in the front stools

to the tune of the song 'Cut the Cake' and I
ordered a double bourbon and coke and drank it
down real fast ordered another one then a pretty
black chick with incredible long legs was dancing and started yelling up at her to do it baby
do it funny how a few drinks and the company
how easy everything else could get turned off
except for the energy of the booze and sex driving me and I kept pounding those doubles
down and didn't realize how drunk I was getting
I was hollering up the strippers and cheering
them on every now and then one of them would
bend over and shake her ass in front of my face
there were girls working the tables I spent about
a hundred dollars talking to one of them as long
as the drinks kept coming she kept talking until
finally it was her turn to dance and then I left
and staggered to one of the all-night porn shops
browsed through magazines and looked at all
the vibrators and double-ended dildos there was
this huge dildo that had to be a foot long and
five inches around man people use those things
like what the fuck but whatever turns you on
then I decided to walk to Chinatown and get
some food and when I was walking down
Washington Street I came closer to a couple who

were making out up against a lamppost looked like a hooker with a fat middle-aged guy in a suit who was pretty drunk and slurring his words the hooker was rubbing his crotch and pulling down his zipper with her other hand she was reaching up inside his suit pocket and in a second she had his wallet pushed him aside and ran down an alley the guy was so drunk he fell over when the hooker pushed him it all happened so fast that by the time the hooker had the guy's wallet out I had walked past them and turned around to see it finish and the hooker had to run right by me even in those heels she could fly and she didn't bother to look up and see me but I got a pretty good look at her before she ran down the alley that's when I ran down the alley after her she must have thought I was the guy chasing her and threw off her shoes and started running faster I shouted out Craig don't run it's me Tony and it took a second or two for it to sink in for him then he stopped in his tracks I took him to Chinatown and ordered a big meal I kept drinking bourbon and cokes trying to get him to eat something but he would only poke his finger at the food on his plate and I urged him to just try a little rice or one spare rib I was real drunk by then past the point of no return it was only luck that Audry was away I told him he could have called me if he needed money and he was going to end up in jail or hurt real bad but he was high and he had about eighty bucks that he stole from the guy and told me to take it as part payment for the money he owed me cause he was going to pay me back every penny it's funny how when you really love someone it's like family and people's faults you just have to live with I mean with all Frank's problems over the years I guess a lot of other guys would have thrown him out on his ass and some of the guys at work always said Luongo you're a fool you're not helping your brother letting him leech off you and I should throw him out and leave him to his own downfall but he was my brother and if you haven't got family you haven't got nothing and with Craig it was like family I remember that night as drunk as I was talking to him like he was one of my children and I was the father it's strange cause in the middle of telling him he needed to change his life he was worth more than what he was doing it hit me that I was already older than my father was when he died and I started to cry in the middle of the restaurant I guess it was the booze but

I couldn't control myself Craig came over sat
close to me in the booth and put his arm around
me and I told him I love you and I don't want to
see you die he said he wasn't going to die and we
left the Chinese place he wanted to go to The
Other Side so I drove to the South End it was
after hours and the place was supposed to be
closed but there were a lot of regulars hanging
around and drinking most of the lights were out
and music was real low everyone in there seemed
high or drunk by that hour of the night the place
had this odd kind of quiet about it like one of
the boys' rooms right after I used to put one of
them to sleep and in the nightlight light they
were still awake Craig and me sat at our usual
table and he rubbed his hand through my hair
we kissed but I don't know if it was cause I was
so drunk or I just was feeling different but I felt
like it wasn't right so I pulled away and told him
I went looking that night to see him to say hello
and find out how things were turning out not to
start things up with him again but I was afraid
now that he was going to keep doing what he
was doing no matter what he winked at me and
smiled we talked a little more and the drinks
kept coming and got stronger until around four

in the morning he passed out I couldn't wake him and the bartender said that we had to get out of there he had to lock up so I picked him up and carried him out he still didn't have any shoes on and the bottom of his nylons were worn through his feet were dirty his dress was coming off him and his make-up all runny and smeared he felt so light in my arms then I put him in the front seat and strapped him in with the seat belt and figured I would take him to a motel some-where at least get him a bed for the night I got my bearings crossed I was drunker than I real-ized and I ended up heading out south of town instead of back into the city so I turned to a side-street so I could make a u-turn and head the other way but it looked like I could drive to the end and head back out in a direction that I thought I recognized cause I was in a part of Roxbury where the old factories and warehouses used to be and at the end of the sidestreet it looked like I had to drive down an alley to get out the other side and when I made it through the alley I was in the open but everything got all bumpy like and the car bounced up in the air and then I was stuck I tried going forward and back but the wheels were off the ground so I got out to look and the car was hung up on railroad tracks and the rear end of the car was caught on one of the rails one look I knew there was no way I was going to get the car off without a tow truck then I started to panic what if a train came but this was old tracks I was pretty sure and didn't get used no more for a few minutes I ran around the car confused then I opened the other door to wake Craig he was pretty groggy and then suddenly my worst fear was happening I could feel a little tremble under my feet and it got bigger I knew a train was coming so I pulled Craig out and dragged him to the side of the tracks and in a matter of a few moments I could see the train's headlight coming down the track and the ground rumbling louder and louder just then there was a huge fucking shriek when the engineer pulled on the whistle I could hear all this hissing squealing and screeching of the train as the engineer hit the brakes and that engine ran into the car and straight through like it was made of paper cut it right in half by the time the train stopped full the last car was a hundred yards off nearly out of sight of the car my car was burning in two squished half pieces one each side of the track I heard voices people

running down the track from the train I picked
Craig up put him on my shoulders and walked
back towards where I thought Mass. Ave. was I
could hear sirens coming from different direc-
tions fire trucks ambulances police and by the
time I got back to Mass. Ave. I could hardly walk
any more so I put Craig down on the steps of a
vacant building he was still out of it I was afraid
if a cop should come by he might get suspicious
then I thought of the car and figured the only
thing I could do at that point was to report it
stolen there was a phone booth a block away so I
called the police to say the car was stolen some
time during the night in the South End then back
to the steps Craig was still dozing with his head
straight down frozen like a statue there in his
beat-up dress no shoes stockings runny and torn
I sat beside him for a few minutes it was quiet
almost no cars on the avenue and no people out
walking over towards the harbor the sky was
changing color getting lighter I didn't know
what the fuck I was going to do with Craig it
was one of the times in my life I felt like I left
time and the world completely outside of it all
maybe what they said the LSD shit was or something I can't really describe that light but some-

how being just a shade different not like sex cause with sex it always seemed just the moment of having an orgasm you leave your body for this ultimate rush but this was slower the light in the sky was changing the closer to the harbor the lighter it was but it wasn't like I could actually see it change I could only see the effects of the change like it lasted for minutes until the silence was broken when a bus went by then a few cars and more cars it got lighter out and people were out walking to bus stops and I had to be in work at nine in the morning myself but I was stuck there I just didn't know what to do by then Craig was starting to wake up I went across the street to a little breakfast place got some muffins and coffee and back over on the steps I made him take some coffee and food I guzzled down my coffee and was feeling dizzy starting to sober up moving into a hangover feeling at the same time I knew I had to get home Audry already probably called twenty times I had to put a good story together if I was going to get out of this one with the car being wrecked and me being out all night but the funny thing was that usually in a situation like that I would feel real bad and guilty and anxious but this time I was so relaxed it wasn't like me something felt different inside like the knot I usually felt inside my stomach was untied I knew that I had to get home as soon as possible and Craig was awake enough starting to get a little sick and shivering I was a little scared he said not to worry it's what always happened until he got something to get better I asked him where did he want to go and waved down a cab we drove him to a little park off Columbus Ave. I left him sitting on a bench he said his friend lived nearby later in the morning he could clean up and change there I gave him all the money I had which was about fifty bucks and kept enough to pay for my cab home I took my suit coat off wrapped it over him and when we drove away I looked back he already had his feet up on the bench and was asleep when the cab pulled up in front of the house the sun was up so was little Tony who was getting ready for work he didn't say much but looked at me kind of funny since I was without my suitcoat and my clothes were messy from all the stuff with the car and carrying Craig he said Ma's been calling all night and the cops called too something about the car and when he left for work I took the phone off the hook to give myself some time to clean up I had to wear a wrinkled shirt and linty suit and none of my shoes had been shined since Audry's mother died so I put an outfit together best I could I always prided myself on having good clothes one of the things I used to think about a lot when I was in display was how good the salesmen got to dress and I knew that if I ever got to be a big-ticket salesman I was going to be known as the best-dressed salesman in the store and since we got discounts I was always buying new suits and shirts and made sure I was the sharpest looking one out on the floor when we were kids we had no clothes and I remember one summer living in a pair of shorts that were Frank's for the whole summer I wore them every day with the same shirt and if it got dirty Ma washed it and hung it out overnight to dry and poor Peter was taller than me and Frank the hand-me-downs fit him real bad and the girls shared what they had Ma I always will remember wore the same dark blue dress and apron every day with stockings and her black shoes and I wanted bad to have nice clothes in high school it kind of worked out that I went to the Voke cause in shop we wore overalls and I didn't have to worry I didn't have enough clothes and had to wear the same things every day and before I got into the shower that morning I stripped down and remember having a great shit it was one of those times when sitting on the toilet can be as good as anything and I mean sex too I didn't understand the new kind of sense of relief I was feeling inside then I flushed and stood in front of the mirror to shave my thick stubs showing through when I had a dark beard shadow my extra chins made my face look even fatter and my belly and tits were hanging and my hair was all gone except for the sides which I combed back and I was staring into the mirror trying to figure out who I was and the sight of my ageing body made me kind of disgusted it seemed like yesterday I got out of the Marines bulky and hard and I raised my arms up flexed at least my biceps and arms were still in shape and I showered dressed and got myself into work on time the first thing I felt when I got there even though I kind of felt it before but it was never as strong soon as I put my foot inside the door I didn't want to be there I didn't want to spend another day of my life there and that was the longest day I watched the clock minute by minute for the first time in years I went blank I didn't make one sale everybody said that I should go home I looked real sick the guys used to say that I was going to die out on the sales floor cause I never called in sick there was a time I think they were right when I was top salesman and digging the job going in with my new suits and shoes and I thought I would stay at Pratt's until I retired but people change and years pass by quicker than you think suddenly you feel different than when you were ten or twenty years younger I knew there had to be a way for me to get out of there part of my feeling so bad was I was working through a hangover it really got to me a couple of times during the morning I got sick and threw up in the men's room leaning over the toilet bowl thinking about Audry what she was going to say I still hadn't talked to her and as the day went on I kept changing my story where I was all night what happened to the car and when she called the store from North Carolina she seemed calm I thought by then she'd want to have my balls she said she was real worried and stayed up all night worrying but she didn't want to talk about it on the phone she would be home the next day we would talk then she was real matter-of-fact and when I tried to

say a few things to feel her out she only said that
she didn't want to talk any more until she was
home and hung up I passed out when I got home
that night then woke up around one in the morning and I couldn't get back to sleep so I was
going to go out for a drive until I remembered
that the car was wrecked so I dressed and went
out for a walk down Broadway to the Sullivan
Square Station the subway cars and buses were
shut down but the Schrafts Candy Company
building was all lit up and its parking lot full
with cars of night-shift employees there were
rumors that the company was closing down and
if they did I don't know what Peter would do he
was there a lot of years and he'd be lost trying to
find a decent job with the economy being bad
when he first started working there he used to
bring home boxes of candy all the time and we
would sit around and eat candy until we almost
got sick Ma too she loved those chocolate cov-
ered cherries and Peter always brought plenty for
her but then after a while the idea of those
chocolates made us sick Peter said it was the
same working in there after a while you couldn't
even stand the smell it was a sweet smell like
fruit when it's just ready to rot in the air that

night coming from the factory I turned around
near the Charlestown line and walked back up
Broadway to the house still not sure what I was
going to say to Audry the next day but somehow
feeling like no matter what I said or what she
believed something inside me was different
something had changed I couldn't quite describe
it cause it was going on for a while I first noticed
it when I fooled around and realized that I could
still look Audry in the eye and even love her after
all she was the mother of my kids and we were
together all those years no one got me any hotter
than she did in those early days it was summer
and there were some incredible sweaty after-
noons sex juices and sweat and sheets soaked
body and hair soaked shit you can't keep that
spark going for twenty years we're only human I
think maybe I loved Craig but not the way I loved
Audry I loved Craig more like a son and in the
time we were getting closer we had a lot less sex
and the sex stopped feeling as good as it did
when we were first together but I must have been
like a kid in a candy store after all those years
with just Audry and then to have him like that
but the sex got less interesting the more I cared
and worried about him Angela really opened my

eyes about how you could just get it on she was always fooling around with someone in the store and could go from that to being a Brownie leader with her daughters so some people don't have all them hang-ups Frank always said he didn't believe in love and he said as far as he was concerned women were all cunts and the only thing they were good for was fucking or having babies and he never met one that wasn't a cunt and the worse he treated them the better they liked it but Frank always picked certain kinds of girlfriends if all you look for is a chick who likes to get shit on that's all you'll find but I always believed in love I could never love anyone the way I loved Audry it didn't mean that we could spend the rest of our life together and everything would be just fine cause as years went on most of the time things seemed like they weren't fine but then just when you think you can't take it any more somehow I would see her in a new way like be able to step back and see her with fresh eyes then I knew that I still thought she was sexy and more I knew that I loved the person she was Audry was really a good person she never asked for much for herself she was a great mother and wife but it was hard year in and year out with

Audry being afraid to go out too much and me
having to do everything on the house and the
errands she didn't want to do she was fine in her
own element like at home with her regiment of
chores and watching her soaps in the afternoon
and calling her mother or her mother calling her
and staying on the phone for an hour and having
supper ready for me and knowing how I felt she
hardly never said no when it came to sex and
before you know it twenty years pass I finished
the house and it was like it needed to be fixed up
all over again the boys were almost on their own
Johnny was in his last year in high school looking into different colleges I was hoping he would
stay in Boston Audry wanted him to go to college in North Carolina he could be near her family we knew he'd get into a good college cause
his grades were straight As it was a matter of
what school he would choose I told him he could
go anywhere he wanted and I would help him all
I could with paying the tuition and helping with
his expenses for books and living the idea that
my son was going to college was unbelievable to
me I was the first one in the family to even graduate high school Josie graduated college and
now Johnny was going to go I only wished Ma

was still alive she would have been proud of
Johnny sometimes I fantasized what it would be
like if Audry and me broke up how I might live
what I would do the boys would be on their own
there was enough money so that Audry and me
would come out of it without too much trouble
over that kind of thing maybe she would be hap-
pier on her own in North Carolina I could sur-
vive I wanted to keep the house maybe buy her
share out or I could sell the house and travel or
open the business with my part of the money all
that stuff ran through my mind that long day at
the store the police believed my story about the
car being stolen and called to say it was found
but totaled when hit by a train when Audry got
back she was a lot cooler than I figured she'd be
she didn't say much at first and put her things
away the boys and me got pizza she had a slice
and smoked a cigarette and kept looking at me
nodding her head a little I didn't know what she
meant by it but it was making me feel uncomfortable the boys went out by then little Tony
had his own car he bought with money from his
job and they took rides down to Revere Beach to
look at girls and when they left and the front
door slammed downstairs I was sitting at the

kitchen table with her it was the quietest I ever remember any time being for only a few seconds it felt like for ever then she asked me really calm so what happened to the car and I told her I went out for a drink with a couple of the guys from work then I wasn't tired so I took a drive up to New Hampshire then took the back road all the way home cause it was such a beautiful summer night and by the time I got back to the city it was late and I was hungry so I went to Chinatown ate some Chinese food at one of the all-night places and when I was finished I went back to the car and it was gone at first I thought maybe I parked it in a different place than I remembered so I walked up and down a couple of streets before I realized it was stolen and by then I spent all the cash I had buying some rounds of drinks at the bar and the Chinese food so I didn't have enough for a cab it was starting to get light I thought of calling little Tony and asking him to come down for me but I knew he'd be sleeping I was all worked up cause of the car getting stolen so I thought I'd walk home it really isn't that far you know from Chinatown to here if you take the backstreets it only took me about an hour maybe a little more and when I got home little

Tony was getting up he said Ma's been calling
and I knew you would be automatically thinking
the worst then I had to go off to work it was the
worst day I ever had on the floor the first time I
went blank and I looked at her and looked at her
right in the eyes and said the police called today
they found the car someone left it on the railroad
tracks a train drove through it and split it in half
she stared back at me into my eyes said you
know Tony it hasn't been easy for me losing my
mother you know how much she meant to me
this is the hardest thing I've ever had to go
through and if I find out that you've been lying
to me I'm telling you right now you are going to
be the sorriest mother-fucker that ever lived
Audry sometimes swore but she hardly never
said fuck and I knew she meant business and I
told her I knew how hard it was losing your
mother I still thought of mine and it still hurt
that she was gone it never goes away she put her
face in her hands and started to cry it wasn't that
I felt guilty about what I did or anything I felt
guilty about lying to her I tried to comfort her as
much as she would let me and for a while later
she was real fragile like that and would break
out crying in the middle of the day or in bed at

night I felt bad even though I couldn't stand her
mother I knew how much she meant to Audry
and since Audry never knew her father her
mother must have been all that much more
important I know that's how I felt even though I
did know my father a little it wasn't like he was a
real father I kind of see it as I was raised by my
mother and that's where the real connection was
my father was a far away thing like when years
passed we even started to joke about him Ma
would tell stories about some of the things he
used to do like fall asleep on the sidewalk in
front of the house it was strange he could make
it all the way home then instead of coming in he
slept out on the sidewalk those kinds of things
aren't funny when they're happening to a family
but when you look back on it after years somehow it's easier to see it and laugh one time when
I was about six or seven it was getting near dark
and my mother thought my father was in the bar
across the street she was just about to strain the
spaghetti and she said for me to run across the
street and tell Pa to come home for supper when
I got to the bar the bartender said he thought my
father was at Jon's Place which was a few blocks
away so I decided to walk down to Jon's Place

when I got there I couldn't find him but one of his friends said he just left and was going to another bar which was a few more blocks away so I walked down to that bar and my father wasn't there there was nobody I recognized so I left and on the way home I took a shortcut through an alley I was a little nervous cause it was getting darker I didn't know the neighborhood and I started running but the alley was a dead end so when I got to the end I turned around to go back out and when I did I noticed there was someone over in the corner and it was a guy and he was jerking himself off he couldn't see me he was facing the other way so I took off running and looked back over my shoulder and he was still jerking off never even noticed me and there was light about half way down the alley and a little bit of it reflected back there enough so that I noticed the guy was bald and I could see a little shine off the top of his head and in that moment I knew it was him and I ran all the way home Ma was all worried and everybody already ate the spaghetti I told Ma I couldn't find Pa and she saved me a dish of spaghetti but I couldn't eat I stayed up that whole night thinking about Pa and what he was doing out there it wasn't that I

didn't know what he was doing because Frank
had already been doing it and told me what it
was but Pa doing it and outside like that it was
the first time I had serious trouble shitting and I
remember then my mother took me to the doctor cause I didn't go for a week and they gave me
some stuff to take when I got older Ma said even
when I was real little I had trouble that way and I
was the hardest one of the kids to potty train
and I was afraid to shit into the potty and would
hold it and the doctor would have to give me
enemas and stuff I guess I understood a little
better about how fucked up Pa must have been
and I kind of pity him more than I hate him or
anything I don't know much about Pa or his
family I met his brother a few times he was a
drunk too and he died from drinking he had
some kids but we never kept in touch with them
but who knows how it was between Ma and Pa I
mean she had five kids and lost three others during  pregnancy and they were only together for
about ten years so he must have been at her a lot
I always got the feeling from what Ma said that
it wasn't something she was all that fond of she
saw it more as a duty as a wife than something
she was supposed to enjoy besides she said to me

more than once when she married my father he was a good looking man she knew he drank but it didn't seem like it was such a problem but in a few years he changed so much that she asked God how could such things happen but she was always more relieved if he got home and passed out after supper than if he kept drinking cause if he kept drinking he got to raising hell and would end up hitting her or forcing himself on her she said he was like a different man all sweaty and unshaven with the booze on his breath poor Ma it was strange how that incident seeing my father that night had an effect on me even if he was in a good mood and wanting to be playful which sometimes he could I couldn't look him in the eye and sometimes I would lay awake at night and see him with his back to me and then I started to have dreams about it and when I got older the dreams changed and sometimes I dreamed I was jerking off somewhere and Audry and the boys saw me and stuff like that I went through a period where I doubted what I saw and figured it wasn't Pa that night but someone who looked like Pa and I buried it for a long time as I grew older except for dreams I kind of forgot all about it and only once in the greatest while it might be a year or more when I least expected it out of nowhere like bang there it would be like I was right there that moment running out of the alley seeing him as I looked over my shoulder when I couldn't go to the bathroom Ma would make boiled prunes and I had to eat them when Ma brought me to Dr Campiglia who was an old Italian doctor with an office on the second floor above Tony the Butcher's in the North End where when Ma did have some extra cash she gathered us up on the bus to the North End and bought ground meat for meatballs and Tony's hot sausages and Ma brought me to the doctor a couple of times he could never find anything wrong with me he spoke only Italian so he talked with Ma I understood a little too and I remember Ma saying something about why they couldn't figure out what was wrong with my stomach and Dr Campiglia in Italian said the problem is not in his stomach it's in his head pointing to his head and Ma said she didn't understand what he meant I didn't neither but when I grew up I understood what he meant when I was blocked up it was never just constipation where you drink some stuff and you shit your brains out that stuff had no effect on me when my system got blocked up it didn't go until it was ready when Audry got back from North Carolina I had a bout then ten days until I was able to go there was something about the way Audry was acting those first few days I expected her to be more pissed and giving me the third degree every time I made a move but she wasn't saying much of anything one day Frank said did I know I was being watched I didn't know what he was talking about and he said by a dick a private dick it was when Frank had his fall at the restaurant he slipped in the kitchen did some damage to his back and was out on workman's compensation the restaurant was fighting him over it he had some kind of trial and his doctor went to court to say how Frank wouldn't be able to work again cause of the damage done to his back in the fall and Frank would need a permanent disability at the time the insurance company was investigating Frank and making sure his claim wasn't fake it was hard to figure with Frank he had us all convinced the way he carried himself real slow around and was walking with a cane but the insurance company was checking him out and Frank said sometimes they had private dicks watch you and try to get pictures and

evidence that you weren't really hurt so he was
on the lookout and noticed someone in a car half
way down the block then he noticed him there
the next day so he was watching from behind his
window on the first floor when I went downstairs and got in my car to drive away and that's
when the guy started up his car and took off following me then it all made sense about Audry
being nonchalant about things since she was
back she hired a private detective to watch me I
didn't say anything to her at first I played it real
cool I was being real cool anyway since she got
back staying close to home getting the insurance
stuff taken care of over the car and then I went
out and bought a new car I don't know why but I
knew somewhere in the back of my mind that
something was going to change soon I was going
to leave Pratt's I was to a point that whenever I
walked into the front door I felt like I was being
strangled the days were longer and longer and
my sales were getting so low that the month
Audry's mother died I was low man in the
department in all my years selling I was never
low man it just didn't bother me cause I didn't
care no more that's the way I was if I cared about
something I could do anything but if I didn't it

was like it could fall off the world as far as I was concerned I let the dick follow me once Frank pointed him out it was pretty obvious and I thought that's what I should do be a private dick this guy wasn't too good at it and when Audry told me what she paid the guy for what he did I figured it had to be one of the best rackets going but after about a week of letting the guy follow me around I was real pissed at Audry and scared too cause if the guy was following me for a while he might have something on me but then I figured out that Audry must have hired him when she got back from North Carolina and if that was so then the guy had nothing on me I didn't know exactly what to do angry as I was that Audry would go behind my back and all but I was thankful that she didn't do it earlier cause she would have had me and with that kind of stuff against me she could have a pretty good case in divorce court and one thing I knew all along was that if something ever happened between Audry and me she wouldn't get any more than what she had coming I waited then one day I told Audry that I found out about the detective that she didn't trust me no more and would stoop to hire a detective to follow me she wanted to know how I found out and I told her it wasn't too hard and I don't know what she was paying him but he wasn't worth much cause I was on to him from the first day I only waited until I could figure out who he was and what he was doing the last thing I would have thought was she would pull something like that so I didn't expect he was someone Audry hired I told her if she didn't trust me how could we even stay together I always trusted her and never gave a second thought that she would do something behind my back she sat down and said that she had some things she wanted to say that's the way Audry was she could keep things inside for a long time and I'd know that something was wrong even from the way she might be keeping to herself and all but she'd stay quiet and calm and finally she would say Tony I have some things I need to say to you and she could sit down calmly and tell me what was on her mind that was the opposite of me I wish I could stay calm and keep things inside instead I feel like I got to explode all the time but that's the way I was and no matter if I tried to stay calm and talk steady I just couldn't so Audry lit a cigarette at the kitchen table and I sat down at one of the

chairs and at that moment I still didn't know
what to expect cause I still wasn't sure that the
dick wasn't following me before Audry got back
if he was and knew about the night with Craig
and me losing the car Audry was going to put it
to me and it would mean the end she said Tony
it's been so hard losing my mother and feeling
like I didn't get any support from you all the
years I stood beside you through everything and
took on your family as my own and lived with
them through all the bullshit I've had to deal
with and that whole time you never gave a tiny
bit of that back to me where my family was concerned you always had this attitude that there's
something wrong with my family and my mother and sisters and maybe so we're all a little
fucked up but Jesus Christ Tony take a look at
your family they're not the Brady Bunch either
you know and you come off like you're so much
above my family and not only that Tony I know
you and I know you can't not be thinking about
fucking around and I don't believe you when you
tell me you were out with the guys for a drink or
took a drive to New Hampshire what is there to
not make me think that maybe even once out of
all those times you weren't where you said and

you were with someone you didn't want me to
know about there was a lot I had to deal with
when I got back from North Carolina Tony I
was already thinking I could never forgive you
for being so fucking cold when my mother was
dying and the way you came right back after two
days and I'm calling from down there and you're
out all night what the fuck did you expect me to
do Tony how much more can I take I had to get a
handle on a few things and a long time ago when
I suspected something my sisters said I should
have you followed and I never did but when I got
back from North Carolina I felt so alone and
helpless I didn't know where else to turn Tony
I'm telling you I was at the end of my rope and
closer than I've ever been to just leaving you you
know everybody loves you and you're the guy
who people always say will do anything for anybody but for Christ's sake Tony the person who
needs you more than anyone needed you more
than ever and you weren't there for me Tony you
weren't there even when you were in North
Carolina your mind was miles away and I wasn't
the only one who noticed it you don't think my
sisters didn't pick up on it cause they did and to
be honest if I was seeing it from where they are

I'd be thinking that my sister is married to a shit just like they were probably thinking not to say they were never married to shits but they had the good sense to get out while the getting was good sometimes I feel that except for the boys I can't think of why I stayed here over twenty years I've done everything you ever asked me to do Tony and you always said that you had no complaints about me as a wife sure you could say you weren't getting enough as you wished you were but who the fuck is Tony the grass is always greener next door you know but maybe next door they think your grass is greener it's all in your mind I don't understand sex Tony and I wish it was better between us but I thought we had other things going between us than just that and then when you can be so insensitive like you were when my mother died I just couldn't believe it I felt like I was living a fool's life for twenty years and one of the few times I ever really needed you you let me down when have I let you down Tony when and by now Audry had gone from this real calm and cool talking to tears and I sat there looking at my hands on table feeling like the biggest piece of shit ever I always said my family came first my whole life I did nothing but sacrifice for my family but I guess you just can't spread yourself out like that someone is going to not get theirs and Audry was right for the most part when I think of it I always took her for granted and never gave it a second thought how she took care of the boys and the house and me and my clothes and did a lot for my mother in those late years when Gina was working and I was always doing for Frank or Peter or Ma or the boys and never for Audry but Audry never asked and always was quiet and if it seemed like something was bothering her and I asked her what was wrong she would say nothing everything's fine so what was I to do but she was right I don't know what it was that made me so stubborn about being there more when her mother was dying even if I did hate the old bitch the way I did I could have helped out at least for Audry's sake there's nothing worse than that feeling when you think so much one way and suddenly you find out that things might not be exactly the way you thought and you have this idea of yourself and bang like out of nowhere the whole thing comes crashing down it wasn't like I thought myself perfect or anything but I always thought Audry had everything she needed

as a wife and sure I was old fashioned about
things and a husband's place and a wife's place
in the home but Audry was old fashioned too she
liked it the way things were she didn't want to be
one of those modern women but the hardest
thing for me to swallow was the fact that Audry
didn't have everything she needed and what she
needed the most I could have given to her and
worse I was more likely to be there for a stranger
and that really hurt but maybe there was some
truth to what she said cause as long as I could
remember I was known as a guy who would do
anything for you and even at work over the years
I would go out of my way for customers and
drive to their houses on the way home if they
were having trouble with their new vacuum or
washer and help them out and all the guys at
work would say I was crazy to do things like that
but it just seemed like the thing to do it wasn't
like I actually thought in my head I'm trying to
be a good guy or anything but if someone needed a ride home and it was in the opposite direction from where I lived who cares you drive them
home or if there's an old person at the supermarket waiting for a cab and it's cold or raining or
even if it's not you smile and offer them a ride

what always was strange to me was how many
people would not take the ride and rather stand
in the cold and pay for a cab I guess I learned all
that stuff from Ma she was always having me do
for people like go to the market with old Mrs
Tedesco who lived downstairs from us and help
her carry her bags home and run down to the
square and do errands for someone in the neighborhood and when it snowed I shoveled our
house and the houses next door and across the
street Ma would never let me take money or anything it was what you did she said I used to go to
the church and help with the chores like raking
leaves in the fall and spring cleaning Ma never
asked she would just say in Italian Saturday
morning you go to the church at nine to help out
I liked church the best when there wasn't a mass
going on there was something that got to me
about the quiet if there were only a few people in
there the way the footsteps would echo and
everyone acting real holy like they were in God's
presence as soon as they walked through that big
door touched their fingers into the holy water
and made the sign of the cross when I was a boy
and wanted to be a priest I would sit in the
church some mornings trying to take it all in and

find the true holy feeling and I would talk to God and ask him please make a sign to me so I can be sure he was really there I never did see a sign but Father Gian Carlo always said you could never really be sure God didn't give those kind of signs it was a matter of having faith that God was there I guess the older I got it was harder for me to keep my faith but even Einstein said there was a God and when I was an altar boy there were always things we would volunteer for like to go to sing Christmas songs to the old people in the nursing home or do a food drive and collect canned food and whatever else for the poor or sell raffle tickets to benefit the sisters who lived at a convent in New Hampshire where they made the communion wafers we took on Sundays there was always something to do and I was always doing and Ma said everywhere she went people said to her that Tony is the nicest boy and I think that was important for Ma cause everyone knew Pa was a drunk and when Frank started getting into trouble she must have felt it was a reflection of who she was so I tried to make Ma proud and it wasn't really that it was that hard or anything I liked people and being around them and doing things they liked me for hey it bothered me too knowing about Pa and how everybody in the neighborhood would hear him going on in the middle of the night and banging things up and then Frank's teachers sending notes home from school when he got into trouble and the principal wanting to talk with poor Ma not even able to speak English crying how she was doing everything she could do to raise a good family so I did what I could to make it a little easier for her it was Audry's saying everything she said to me that night that made me aware maybe I should have been doing some of that stuff for Audry too what hurt most was to think how long Audry had felt these things and not said much oh maybe once in a great while but mostly Audry was the kind of person that everything was ok when you asked her and suddenly I was this mean bastard who cared more about strangers than his own family I wondered how many times a day or a week or a month I might have let her down like the time I did some carpentry work for Bonnie Wheeler the store cashier and it took me three or four of my days off and I wouldn't take any money that was ten years before and Audry was jealous cause she thought I had the hots for Bonnie I guess I did  I had the hots for everyone but that's not why I did things for people the time when Peggy LaRonga our neighbor's car broke down I drove her to Providence to see her sister who was dying in the hospital Peggy was seventy years old I just did it cause that's what I do but Audry said all those times I was off doing things for other people did I ever once think that she might need me to do something for her or maybe the boys needed me to do something for them I lost it at that moment cause suddenly after all the years of living and working for my family it was like I never did a fucking thing and I picked up one of the kitchen chairs and smashed it to pieces screaming to her what the fuck is it she wanted from me Audry cried she said that's just what I mean Tony some things never change I tore out of the house in a rage and drove but I didn't want to drive to New Hampshire so I drove up to the north shore and ended up in Gloucester at one of the beaches with a little footbridge it was getting dark there were only a few people walking on the beach I was never a strong swimmer the tide was going out I knew if I really wanted I could jump in swim out as far as I could and I would never make it back but I was too scared and I had this feeling like I would explode there was no place for all my anger and rage to go like I could just smash my head on a wall just to relieve myself I walked down the beach toward some rocks and on top of this big hill of rocks was a mansion and the lights were just coming on I wondered if the same fucking stuff went on in those places and what were they eating how did they fuck and don't tell me the lady of the house in her quietest hours didn't use her God-given fingers and think about getting the living shit fucked out of her by her Greek gardener and what the fuck did they do with all that space I thought about Craig the night when I last saw him I was already driving my brand new Toyota and he was probably high or giving someone a blow job so he could buy drugs and I thought of Ma and Audry and the boys all these different scenes from my past were racing in my mind like on a movie screen I loved Audry so much and the thought that I could hurt her so much made me feel like I was a complete failure and the biggest piece of shit on earth just like Pa was and all this stuff was whirling around in my head so fast I thought if it didn't stop I would go crazy it was hard for me to accept that maybe I wasn't the

father and husband I thought I was and what
Audry said was it was more than just working
and paying bills and looking good to the neigh-
bors I knew that but it was her words that everything always had to be my way that really
stabbed me too like all the years we were together it was ok with her that what I said goes it
wasn't like I never asked her for her opinion no
matter what we were planning I always asked her
what she thought and listened then went right
ahead and did exactly what I wanted when it
wasn't always the best for everybody I made
choices that were sometimes the best for me like
insisting Johnny go to Boston College so he can
live at home instead of New York University
where he wanted to go Johnny got into a bunch
of schools but I thought if he could get into a
local college it would be best so he could live at
home and that way we could save on the tuition
and we'd all be closer and Audry asked did it
ever cross my mind that maybe Johnny wanted
to live away from us for a while why would he
want to live away from us I couldn't understand
and besides he was too young to be living in
some place like New York City and Audry said
that Johnny was almost the same age I was when

I joined the Marines and went off to Korea no
matter how old your kids get I guess you always
see them like children and when I got to the end
of the beach there was a big sign that said private property keep out where the grounds of the
mansion started and some lights were lit up
bright from the windows of the place I was
tempted to climb up the rocks and have a peek in
but I figured they had dogs or something Frank
always liked the voyeur thing when we were kids
a few times he took me down the street and we
hid in the bushes where a lady who lived alone
kept her shades up while she did chores around
the house naked Frank beat off but I was too
scared and even when Frank was older he always
kept a pair of binoculars right by his window
cause he liked checking out windows at night
and said it wasn't watching them have sex that
he liked most but what he liked more than anything was to watch a naked chick clean her
apartment they say the rich folks can get pretty
wild and I started to imagine some kinky orgy
going on up there but I knew that sooner or later
I had to go back home and face Audry and when
I got home she was in the bedroom watching
television with the door closed the apartment

was dark except for the television light coming out between the door and the frame I tripped in the kitchen cause the broken chair pieces were still on the floor and that wasn't like Audry in the past she would have picked them up like the time I got mad and threw a pot of boiling spaghetti on the kitchen wall and she spent an hour scraping it all up and Gina found out what happened she heard the noise downstairs and she said sometimes I was just like Pa I tapped on the bedroom door before I went in and called her name she was watching the screen on her side of the bed with her back to me I sat on the edge of the bed and called her name again only quieter in the months after that when I was at work I tried to get back that enthusiasm that I had when I was number one I couldn't there were days when I knew if I really applied myself I could be tops in the department again I could still sell double and triple service policies and hardly never sold advertised merchandise all the guys had their own methods of trading up some just made it seem like that cheap washer was the biggest piece of shit going others like Mike Cordano would take the order right away and only at the very last second when he was ready to

ring the sale up he would stop and say to his customers hang on one second and go into the back
room for a smoke and come out and say that he
just called the warehouse and they had a couple
of discontinued washers there that were far
superior to the one they were purchasing and for
a few dollars more he could make sure they got
one if they ordered today one of the guys would
take the order for the advertised washer then
write the order on top of the top-of-the-line
washer and not say a thing and nine out of ten
by the time he was done writing up the sale the
customer would ask some kind of question
about the top-of-the-line like how much does
this one cost and he would roll up the slip place
it in his pocket and then go into his pitch I
always told the customer everything they wanted
to know about the advertised machine and said
what a great deal it was and how happy I would
be to take an order for one but would they allow
me just a few minutes to show them what a real
top-of-the-line machine can do and it was how
you got them over there and then convinced
them that if I was going to purchase a machine
for myself this is the one I wanted not everyone
went for it and sometimes you might start to

trade them down to one of the mid-line machines but in my day I sold more top-of-the-line than anyone but somehow I wasn't satisfied any more I felt that I was still young enough that I wanted a new challenge the stocks had reached the bottom and some people said they might even start to come back a little if Ronald Reagan was elected president so my profit sharing could get better it would be a good time to look around for my business again Audry was all for it though she said she didn't want me to risk all the profit sharing and savings I'd worked too hard to lose it all if something should happen but if the stocks would only come up a little I'd still stand to make some money and I'd use that for the business and still keep the savings which was a good amount though Johnny's college was going to take a chunk of it Johnny and Audry got their way and Johnny was in college at New York University he got some of it on scholarship cause he was a good student but I was paying the rest and his spending money down there but I was real proud and one of the happiest days of my life was the first check I had to write for his tuition no matter how hard I tried I couldn't get him to go to Boston College I would have put my foot down and insisted that's where he go but Audry and me were trying to work things out between us and one of the things that always bothered her most was when I got to pulling my weight around and having things my way that night I got back from the drive to the beach and sat down on the edge of the bed we talked for hours it was like when we were first together there was always something deep between us sometimes you can just lose touch with that and she cried in my arms and I cried we talked about the old days when we met at the store and how fast time goes by how some things seemed better than either one of us hoped but in some ways they were worse and I promised her I would try to change and that sometimes it was hard for me too us being different cause I was the kind of guy who liked to be sociable and Audry liked to keep to herself and didn't like being with people besides her family she knew I was always into sex and over the years it got kind of hard for me cause she had her own hang-ups being shy about certain things as parents at least we were both proud of the boys they were good kids never got into any serious trouble and Johnny going to college we must have been doing something right it was a long time since we had sex but that night when our hugging started getting a little heavy we started kissing and did it real good for the first time in a long time it was our usual way it seemed like no matter how you might think you want something different when we got into it with each other it was exactly the same way we kissed a while and I played with her titties I licked them then she laid me back on the bed and jerked me off and did me a little then I turned her over opened her legs and ate her starting nice and easy and building up then she said to me come inside her and I slid in we kissed and went at it for a while kissing hard me playing with her tits I always tried to wait for her to come before I did sometimes it was hard cause I would be ready and she wouldn't be so I would hold off by trying to get my mind outside of what we were doing for a few seconds think about work or something and that would give me the break I needed to go a few more minutes Audry had real spastic loud orgasms but over the years she kind of started to do this heavy but quiet breathing groan instead cause she was afraid of the boys hearing her and there were times when I wondered if she ever faked it and I

asked her and all she said was that I shouldn't
ask her things like that it made her uncomfortable in the old days we could do it out in the living room or kitchen I used to bend her over the
kitchen table and once I even got her out into the
hallway in the middle of the night and we did it
on the stairs of my old apartment she was really
turned on she kept asking what if somebody
comes but she was hotter than I ever seen her but
that night of the big scene when we did it even
though it was our usual way we had done it time
and time again something was a little different
and when Audry came she had these long shivers
like the night she came all those years ago on the
steps in the hallway and when we finished we
slept really deep it was the longest sleep I had in
years and in the morning it was quiet but it was
like somehow a lot of the tension that had been
in the air and building and building wasn't there
any more and so after that things just went on
for me and Audry I knew how close she was to
leaving me and the more I thought about it the
more scared I got but me making threats that I
would do something crazy or anything like that
wouldn't work it was like I was fighting for my
life to keep her and we didn't do it for a while

after that but we were closer than we were in a
long time and started doing more touching we
went to New York City to help get Johnny started at school Audry cried when we were driving
home since little Tony was still living with us
Johnny was the first one to leave home little
Tony wasn't going anywhere they loved him
at the sporting goods warehouse and he got a
couple of raises and he bought himself a used
Caddie I thought it was too much car for him
but that's what he wanted this big white four
door Caddie and the first month he had it he got
into an accident he said it wasn't his fault but he
was cited for reckless driving I told him as long
as he was living with us he still had to live under
my rules and if he got into any more trouble
with the car he was going to have to sell it it was
hard for me to discipline little Tony I felt bad for
him being so big and in the time he was out of
high school he got even bigger and he didn't
seem to have a lot of friends and the ones he had
only hung out with him cause he had the big car
they could drive around the only thing he
seemed interested in outside of work was pool
and he played pool almost every day I didn't
know anything about the game but I heard he

was real good at it so I couldn't stop him from doing one of the only things he was good at doing it made him feel good about himself knowing people thought he was a good pool player he wasn't home very much and most of the time he was working or at the pool hall or driving around with his friends looking for chicks we let him come and go as he pleased and with Johnny off at college in New York suddenly the house was so different and quiet with just me and Audry it forced us to be more in touch with each other cause without the boys there were no distractions it was just the two of us face to face Audry had dinner ready when I got home from work and we had breakfast together in the morning she still didn't like to go out much so I did the shopping and ran the errands when I was working she talked to her sisters on the phone and watched the soaps months went by and I had a hard time trying to understand how fast the time had gone with just the two of us alone again in some ways it was like the old days we started talking about more deeper things than the weather or what the boys needed or taking my mother to the doctor what was the news how much business I wrote at the store and what was the store gossip but we were talking about things like death and love and life it wasn't like when we were first together when we talked about all those things back then I don't think we really knew what we were talking about so we had this great excitement like we were going to take on the world together then before you know it the boys need shoes again or Teresa took Anna and left cause my brother Peter was hitting her again years go by with a bunch of these kinds of things happening but now with Ma dead and Audry's mother dead twenty years of struggling to keep our marriage together and raising the boys it was like we were in our twenties again cause we still didn't know anything about all the big things in life but it was like we knew we didn't know and weren't going to be able to figure it out that made it easier we often found ourselves looking at each other and shrugging our shoulders thinking who knows at the exact same time I never saw Craig again after that last time when the car got wrecked he never called and I never went out looking for him there were days when I felt like it all never happened then there were days when it was too real like it happened yesterday and it was going to come back to haunt me

and it did when everybody started talking about
the Aids thing this new sex disease that made
herpes look like a runny nose it was getting
passed around mostly by queers and people were
dying and then I started to get scared for him
and then scared for me then they said there was a
way you could get tested to see if you had it it
was a strange thing the way you didn't just die
from it but you could catch a cold and die from
that I didn't want to get tested I didn't want to
know and then I thought about Audry cause me
and her had been getting on during the time I
was with Craig and they said it wasn't just sex
between two guys sex between anyone and you
could catch it and people who used drugs and
needles were getting it too it was kind of like this
wrath of God was coming down on everything
or something and one day at the store when I
saw Angela then I remembered her and we didn't
go all the way but we sure were swapping some
spit and I thought about how if you got it everyone you got it on with after that might get it and
pass it on to everyone they got it on with when I
thought about all the guys he was with and that
he used needles for shooting drugs I figured he
was a prime person to get the fucking disease

and then after all the times we did it there was a
good chance I had it it was never that I was
afraid of dying or anything but who would ever
think you could die from fucking though when I
was talking about Aids with the guys at work
one of them said people used to die from the
clap all the time and I never thought of that but
at first I was as worried about Audry and the
boys finding out as I was about dying then
people were getting it from blood donations and
stuff and it was like a black death who would
have known after how far mankind had come
sex would be killing people off the older I got I
was less religious it's not that I stopped believing
in God but I stopped going to church every week
but during that time there were some Sunday
mornings I got up and went to mass and Audry
didn't know what was up with me and kept asking was I all right but I was going to church and
praying a lot and asking God not to let me get
Aids like with all the fucking problems in the
world he would listen to me and stop me from
getting it but I was so afraid I didn't know what
else to do I couldn't go to the doctor cause he
was our family doctor and I heard there were
these clinics where you could go and they didn't

take your name just gave you a number and you call back a few days later but then I realized that I didn't want to know if I had it I had it and I might have even given it to my own wife like think of it killing your own wife by making love to her it was all too fucking much so I went to church and prayed for Craig and hoped he didn't have it and that maybe he got himself straight and went back to school like he said he would but for months I couldn't think of anything but the fact that I could have Aids and I might be dying and maybe Audry and Angela too I knew I should get myself tested cause if I did have the disease I owed it to them to tell them but how could I I wondered even if I did have it could I go to them and tell them Audry especially how so I got all the information I could and called numbers where you could ask questions and I had to do it all on the sly so no one would know and they still weren't sure how it worked but it took a while before you even showed it in your body so I could have it and it wouldn't show if I got tested anyway one of the first signs was that you lose weight so I started forcing myself to eat and drink things like milkshakes and doing exercises again it was the first time in maybe fifteen years I had done any exercises I could only do a few push-ups and sit-ups at a time I came a long way from my days in the Marines when I could do fifty push-ups like nothing I started walking when I was feeling stressed instead of taking rides since I had a car I took rides and when I drove around I used to get something to eat at some point during the ride like donuts or a hamburger but then I started walking and I stopped eating cause it was harder to eat while I was out walking then when I was in my car whether it was in the day or the middle of the night if I was worried about things I did my best to keep it from Audry but sometimes she would say to me what's wrong Tony you seem like your mind is a thousand miles away one time when I was out walking I thought about Craig and without a second thought I walked up to a phone booth and took out my wallet cause I still had the number of his friend where he used to crash it wasn't that I wanted to see him I just wanted to know was he ok and maybe his friend knew but the number was no longer in service I got this cold chill over me walked for hours it wasn't that what I did was wrong or that I felt bad about it it was that others would think it was wrong and

what a way for everyone to find out to have me
and maybe Audry die because I cheated what a
crazy fucking life I just couldn't understand how
one thing could lead to another in such a huge
way but that's the way things were people were
sick and dying all over the country I'm sure there
were guys out there who already passed it on to
their wives and I wouldn't be the first one like I
always said nothing you could think of hasn't
already been done and after about a year went
by it was hard not to think about what happened
between me and Craig cause day to day it was in
the news and everyone was talking about it they
said straight people were passing it along too
and almost overnight people who used to fool
around a lot started getting scared I could see it
around the store how all the people single or
married it didn't make no difference were changing their habits and had to be thinking to themselves about who they'd been fucking and who
that person had been fucking and when I think
of it there was a lot of fucking going on in the
seventies not to say there's not always a lot of
fucking going on but it was much more open at
least cause while there was always some shifty
stuff going on at the store when I started working

there it was in the seventies when all the guys were letting their hair down and the chicks wearing those hot pants and what else one week Bill Nardella fucked four different chicks from the store and even he was saying it was time to be more careful he was using rubbers again even if the chicks were on birth control that last year at the store I had one of my best years of earnings ever but a lot of it was cause the prices on all the merchandise had gone up when there was a price increase there was an increase in my commissions but I daydreamed my shifts away thinking about when I would be out of there it was like a slow hum my life then going to work coming home having dinner with Audry watching television going to bed early and when I couldn't sleep I took a walk the worst part of the night was always around four in the morning I didn't mind being up at five or three or one but four was the time I dreaded the most it was when my mind was the least in control and my thoughts would race and it was so dark and quiet like it wouldn't end then in the fall the guy who owned the storefront across the street put it up for sale again he had been renting to a woman who started a beauty salon but she went out of business at first

he wanted too much money it wasn't that I did-
n't have it I didn't think it was worth what he
was asking and I told him what I was willing to
pay and said if he called me within a month I'd
take it after that my next offer might be less and
three weeks later he called and said he would
take my offer and suddenly this new fear took
hold of me like it was really going to happen
after all the years of thinking about it and wish-
ing it I was going to start my own business I
went into the store the very next day and gave
my notice all the guys said I was crazy to leave
now after all the years I built up and I should not
forget all those before me who tried to leave for
something better and were sorry I was too old
now to be risking everything I had what if it
didn't work out I'd lose all my profit sharing my
savings even my house and in some ways they
had a point I thought about all those things but
in other ways they were just jealous cause over
the years one thing was certain that they were all
as unhappy as me there some of them were miserable and hated Pratt's and all of them smoked
too much and had ulcers and took stuff for their
stomachs they were under so much pressure to
sell and selling just came so natural for me it

never was that stressful from where I was I just got bored with it and a lot of them would have left if they could and Tony Deluca always talked about opening a horse stable and giving riding lessons and Nick Luciano always talked about buying a bigger boat and taking people out on fishing trips but they always just talked any of them could have done it if they wanted but they were afraid that if it didn't work out they'd be stuck without jobs to make enough for their lifestyle and all their savings gone maybe their houses too but look how miserable you all are I said but secretly they were glad I was going even though I wasn't top salesman any more they always had it against me the way I came in like I did and outsold them all year after year and I told Ms Clarkson the new personnel manager I didn't want any kind of party or anything cause anyone who worked at the store as long as I did would automatically get a party of some kind she said people would want to throw me a party I had a lot of friends in the store but I told her flat out that I wouldn't come so she would be best to discourage it I was keeping real close to home I only went out for walks or to run errands otherwise I was home with Audry or working it

was a long time since I'd last been with Craig
and I was feeling good and lost some of my extra
weight from all my walking and push-ups and
sit-ups and was hoping that if nothing happened
to me by then it probably wasn't going to happen though they said it could stay inside you for
longer before it showed up and started doing
things I wondered about Craig sometimes where
he was how he ended up and I still sometimes
thought of him when I jerked off but it was
strange no matter how hard I tried I couldn't
remember exactly what he looked like once in a
great while his face would come flashing by in
my mind when I didn't expect it like when I'd be
in the middle of talking to a customer or taking
a turn while I was driving in the car but if I tried
to remember his face I couldn't only little things
like his light skin or his blond hair or his blue
eyes or the earrings he wore when he was dressed
up or how he could bat his eyelashes when he
had all that stuff on them and I always remembered how skinny he was like when I put my
arms around his waist he used to wear boys-size
blue jeans and even they would hang off him but
it's that way with people you know in the past
even people you loved and slept with unless you

saw them or had photographs to remind you
there was no way you could remember them
perfectly I still used to think of Laura great love
of my life besides Audry and maybe in her own
way more important than Audry and couldn't
remember everything about her only her freckles
or her curly hair little things like that I couldn't
picture her completely in my mind so it was
strange to jerk off thinking about somebody in
the past cause if I didn't remember how they
looked you kind of had to imagine it and so it's
not like jerking off to that person but jerking off
to who I imagine is that person with Craig and
me the first few times we did it it was animalistic
cause after I saw him a while it changed and the
sex was never like it was those first few times my
feeling about jerking off was always it doesn't
matter what you fantasize about it's only in your
head and even though me and Audry had practi-
cally stopped doing it I still liked jerking off as
much as when I was a kid I could do it all day if I
had the chance got to the point with Audry and
me we spent our time together and I kissed her
when I went off to work and when I got home
and we put our arms around each other at night
in bed but that's about as far as it went it both-

ered me that we lost that part of our marriage but as I got older I felt less and less shitty that I wasn't able to fuck all the time Frank never let up no matter what he always had a new girlfriend it was always the same too he kept them around for a year or maybe two then started cheating on them until they found out and eventually they'd leave and the new girlfriend move in but sometimes it took longer than you would think I could never believe how women could cling to Frank one of his girlfriends even told him that she didn't care if he cheated she loved him and would be there for him when he got home he had to throw her out by force and then there were the two that got into a fist fight at the bar at the tavern and they had to call the cops in Frank loved it especially since his new girlfriend beat up his old girlfriend and when I left the store to start the ice cream business he wanted to be part of the business and did every different kind of pleading and begging but I stayed firm I knew him better than he knew himself he already had been running a book business on the side since he was officially given a disability from his fall at the restaurant he walked around with a cane and a little bit of a limp which I was never sure he faked or was real but he was running his own little racket making plenty and collecting a monthly disability check but he still didn't have no money he offered to have his monthly disability check signed over to me if I took him in as a partner I told him in twenty years you never paid me a nickel in rent while you live in my house now you want me to take you in as a business partner it was so easy for me to do all the money business over buying the property the lawyer I hired said it was all just moving paper around and he was right one day we showed up and signed a bunch of things and it was over I signed a bunch of things at the store to transfer my retirement and my profit sharing money and suddenly I owned this property across the street from the house I paid cash and still had some profit sharing left over to buy all the things I would need to fix the place up it needed a lot of work and I planned to spend the winter doing all of the work myself and then have a grand opening in the spring so I left the store after twenty-five years just like that I worked right up to my last day and in twenty-five years I never called in sick and some people thought it wasn't the right thing to do to say you

didn't want a party cause everyone who worked
there as long as I did got a party but on my last
day Mr Kelly the new manager called a meeting
in the furniture department before the store
opened and made this nice speech about me and
what kind of employee I was all the years and
handed me this giant card everyone in the store
signed and some just said good luck other people wrote some nice things about how much they
liked me and all that the guys in the department
said that they finally drove me out like they said
they would when I started in sales and Angela
wrote how much she'll remember that one time
we worked inventory day together inventory day
was when they close the store down once a year
and everyone had to do inventory for a day with
a partner but Angela and me never did inventory
day together as partners I knew what she meant
thank God Audry didn't cause she read the card
but that made me feel real good cause I often
wondered did she ever think of me any more like
I knew she had a few more flings in the store but
after Aids I think she started keeping it close to
home like a lot of people but I still thought of
her and that night in the car her doing herself
and doing me I went home that night finished

my last shift after all those years getting to know
so many people many of them were working at
the store when I started in display I said goodnight to everyone on my way out and I never
once went back it wasn't on purpose I told everyone I was nearby and I wouldn't be going
nowhere and I'd come in and say hi but I never
did and before long it's too long and not long
ago they closed the old Central Square store
down it was the oldest Pratt's store in the country and they closed it down to put a mall in there
with all these little stores inside so I never saw
anybody again and in all the time none of them
ever came by the ice cream store like they said
they would but that's the way things go I left my
last shift on a Saturday the very next Sunday
morning I was across the street at the store and
for the next seven months worked morning noon
and night by myself seven days a week getting
the place in working condition everything needed repair from floor to windows and walls I
stripped banged and painted it was almost like
building the place from the ground up after
Christmas that year I started to talk with people
about franchises who had soft ice cream who
had homemade the money was in soft cause you

whipped it up so much but I decided that I didn't want to franchise who needed them I bought all the necessary freezers and equipment and opened my own place without any debt to any-body else and called it Tony's Ice Cream and I bought my ice cream from who I wanted to buy it from and I sold soft ice cream and regular ice cream and I had a company in Rhode Island do this great sign for me and it came just in time for when we opened I was still putting the finishing touches on the outside paint and I needed at least one more big freezer but I figured I could make it through the first season I didn't want to overextend myself so that if something went wrong I'd be screwed and I knew if I sold a lot of ice cream I'd go buy some somewhere quick if I couldn't keep enough in the freezers I already had I could buy supermarket ice cream if I need-ed and scoop it into a cup and make good return then after all the planning and building I did I decided people didn't hang out much inside ice cream places so I took out the big front picture window boarded it up put two take-out win-dows there and the city said it would be ok to put some tables and chairs out front for people and Audry thought I was crazy out there at midnight keeping the neighborhood awake with my sawing and banging but I had my mind made up to open on May first and nothing was going to stop me after months of work and trips to the lumber yard and the hardware store then trying to buy all the equipment I went around looking to buy used but most of it was all overpriced fucking junk so I bought all brand new stuff it cost me a fortune and I had to go into my savings which I didn't want to do but I used up all my profit sharing and retirement money faster than I thought I would then at twelve o'clock in the afternoon on the first of May we opened I took out an advertisement in the *Somerville Journal* for the four weeks in a row announcing our opening and we had big balloons and on Memorial Day I rented one of those searchlights that shoots into the sky and that was the first weekend I did any business up to that time there were days when it was cold and rainy I was there from twelve to ten and didn't sell one ice cream it was real scary for a while and I was afraid if any of the guys from the store ever dropped by and saw that I was doing no business I would be embarrassed I knew I had to hang in there but I was tapping into the savings heavier than I wanted to Audry told me that I shouldn't do things like rent the big light which was expensive but I always felt that you had to spend money to make money and that summer I worked seven days a week from twelve when I opened to ten at night closing time and Audry helped out a lot or just hung around cause she was across the street she would bring me my supper every night work the counter while I ate I didn't really do much business that first year I started to think that I fucked up and would be sorry just like the guys at work told me would happen but what I remember most was how good I felt to be sitting there every day in my own building running my own business and having nobody to answer to it was the best feeling and I knew that the first year would be a rocky one then that summer Johnny didn't come home from school in the spring he was going to stay in the city and get a job for the summer I was pissed cause I was counting on him to come home and help work the store with me since I was paying for his college and I threatened that if he didn't come home I wouldn't pay for his school the next year and he said to me over the phone like he was talking to a stranger instead of his father if you want to do that Dad

it's your right but I'll stay here anyway and take
out student loans for school I couldn't believe he
could fucking talk to me that way it's not like he
talked to me disrespectful or anything it was like
he was his own boss and he didn't need me and it
hurt real bad Audry talked me into giving in she
always hit me with the same line that when I was
his age I was across the world in Korea think
how my mother must have felt and it was just
that no one was around any more Gina finally
married this older guy who was divorced and
had two kids in college but he seemed like a nice
guy and he had some money from a business he
owned installing air conditioners in cars and
they bought a house on the south shore and I
was lucky if I saw her more than once a month
but we talked on the phone a lot and her daughter missed Somerville and all her friends at first
but then she started to like the new place and
Peter's wife threw him out finally after she
couldn't take his shit and he was giving his
daughter a hard time too when she divorced him
she had so much evidence against him from all
the restraining orders and police files that she
got the house and most of the money Peter had
and he moved back in the second floor after

Gina moved out and he was kind of down and
out drinking a bit feeling bad for himself and
saying that she got all his money and I let him
stay there free and he paid his utilities little Tony
finally got married and lived in Manchester New
Hampshire he worked for the highway department cause his wife's family had connections up
there and they had two kids and it was really the
thing that made me realize how fast time goes by
when you see your kids with their own kids
before you know it another chunk of years goes
by like you didn't even notice and who would
have figured little Tony the kid from the city
moving to New Hampshire but Manchester was
like the city anyway and he still played pool a
few nights a weeks the ice cream store turned out
better than I ever hoped and once I figured all
the ins and outs of running the place I opened
from Memorial Day at the end of May to
Columbus Day in October every year and made
enough money to take the rest of the year off
mostly Audry and me just stayed home we didn't
do much she usually went down to North
Carolina for a month during the winter and I
went down for a couple of weeks that was as
much as I could stand her sister Sue had broken

the family record and was on her fourth husband
and I said being the youngest she'd probably
break her own record more than once Johnny
finished college then got a master degree and
became a math teacher in New York City he
loved it there and he never said anything but
Audry and me didn't neither he was a good looking guy and he never had a girlfriend so we kind
of knew it wasn't that it bothered me cause it
didn't long as you're a good person I don't care
who you sleep with what kind of bothered me
was that he couldn't tell us or at least felt that he
couldn't he never did I thought of telling him I
knew and didn't care but the few times I saw him
it didn't seem like the thing to do I worried
about Aids too but Johnny was a smart kid and I
figured he knew how to be careful we didn't see
him much maybe once or twice a year on holi-
days we saw little Tony and his family a lot they
would come down on Sundays for dinner and
Audry made macaroni and gravy little Tony got
bigger and bigger and the doctor told him he
would die young if he didn't stop eating so much
but he wouldn't listen his kids were beautiful he
had a boy and girl and I feel lucky in a way cause
looking back to when I was a kid being on wel-

fare and my family never having nothing and
then me doing as good as I did and the house all
paid for and the store property all paid for and
suddenly after all the years they stopped rent-
control in Cambridge and overnight the property values in Somerville started to go up higher
and higher who would have known and all these
real estate agents started getting in touch telling
me how much property was worth and I had a
small fortune on my hands and that's what this
country is about that a guy like me could start
with nothing and later be leaning on the counter
of his own business on his own property looking
across the street at his own house and my brother Frank sitting out at one of the tables on the
sidewalk with his notebook and beeper and cane
he's probably worth more than me though his
goes right back out fast as it comes in there was
no way to stop Frank from doing what he wants
to do when I told him I was worried about the
cops he said every cop that drove by knew what
he was doing that's the way things went when
was I going to smarten up and quit working so
hard and I did think that if the real estate prices
were going to keep going up at some point I
would sell it all and maybe me and Audry move

down to someplace warm like Arizona or something and buy a nice house with a pool and big
television for her and just live out our days I got
to hand it to Audry even in her fifties she looked
good and kept her figure me I let it all go and
after the ice cream store was doing good I started shaving my head I don't know why but one
morning I woke and got this urge and shaved my
head there was really only the sides to shave the
top was bald already Audry said I looked kind of
scary to people but I got into it and the customers got used to it and the kids liked it and
every morning I got up and shaved my head
before I showered and sometimes I still looked
close in the mirror to see if any bugs might be
crawling around somewhere even though I knew
there's no place for them to crawl and the one
thing that never did change is that I never
stopped thinking of sex even though me and
Audry only did it maybe once a year I still jerked
off every chance I could I never stopped Frank
was in his glory sitting out there all day and
night he said what better way to watch chicks
than at the ice cream store with all the young
moms coming down their summer clothes and
those bored wandering eyes checking out the

young dudes and the little girls so young I don't
want to know in their short shorts and little tit
tops the older I get the better they look I know
what they mean by dirty old man now that I'm
there I don't feel guilty one bit getting off on a
twelve-year-old girl licking the top of a vanilla
cone I mean what the fuck

## Gas Station

Rear-end fluid, battery acid, exhaust hoses, floor jacks and leaky gaskets; a dusty black 1963 Ford Galaxie over by the air pump, torn pin-ups in the compressor room, chainsmoking mechanics listening to a tinny radio – the rust and grease and grime of the gas station, the rhythms of work and talk, are detailed with such precision in Joseph Torra's first novel that the locality becomes universal. As Jimi Hendrix and Vietnam rumble on in the background, an Italian-American teenage boy grows up working in his dad's gas station in Massachusetts, awkward with his father and not too hot at mounting snow tires or dismantling engines. In *Gas Station* Joseph Torra has written an extraordinary and superb coming-of-age novel in the great American blue-collar tradition, and one which has echoes of another working-class son of Massachusetts, Jack Kerouac.

'This is the genuine article. It's dirty and prickly, quirky and poetic, everything writing ought to be' Geoff Nicholson

'His deadpan tone leads to touches of humour and pathos, while his highly compressed prose at times achieves the intensity of poetry. Torra's extraordinary, challenging first novel offers a highly charged cameo of blue-collar small town America' *Observer*

'Torra makes a visit to the coffee shop and the chat of the mechanics into a kaleidoscope of high poetry in which the rhythms of everyday life are beautiful not banal' *Guardian*

'Stick with it . . . it does eventually fire on all cylinders ★★★★' *Uncut*

'Simply as a story it's interesting, but the story-telling has a wonderful sense of imagination, intelligence, economy and originality. I loved the feeling of being both inside and outside the story, a participant and an observer. The way Mr Torra flows from one event to another, to a memory, to an observation is quite an accomplishment, and no matter where the flow goes it is always natural, logical and very human. AND, this book is always a joy to read'
Hubert Selby Jr

'Joseph Torra writes with a love and care that brings it all back to where it came from, that very first time of our lives' Robert Creeley

'If words were lug nuts he'd spin them in ways the guys down at the garage never dreamed of'
*New York Times*

'Beautiful first novel . . . both lyrical and true'
*Publishers Weekly* Books of the Year, 1996

0 575 06803 5
£6.99

# My Ground

Following the teenage boy in *Gas Station* and the department-store salesman in *Tony Luongo*, the narrator in the third and final part of Joseph Torra's **My Ground** trilogy is a middle-aged female housecleaner. Again, the concern is with the lives of blue-collar workers in Massachusetts, and with the attempts of an individual to carve an identity for his or herself in a harsh world.

*My Ground* is the story of Lauren Bell's less than stable life of failed relationships, a difficult childhood, weight problems and ECT treatment. In a bleak but powerful work the sense of the span of a human life is skilfully compressed into a short novel, and the various strands are pulled together at the close into a horrific climax.

0 575 06849 3
£6.99
January 2001